PART II
PERSONAL POWER®
— CLASSIC EDITION —

The Most Successful Personal Achievement Program of All Time: 7 Days to Discover What You Want & How to Get It

D1097250

DAY	SESSION TITLE	AUDIO CDs
DAY 1	**The Key to Personal Power:** Harnessing the Power of Decision	1
DAY 2	**Pain & Pleasure:** The Controlling Forces That Direct Your Life	1
DAY 3	**The Power of Associations:** The Key to Shaping Your Destiny	1
DAY 4	**The 3 Steps to Lasting Change:** The Science of Neuro-Associative Conditioning	1
DAY 5	**The Goal-Setting Workshop:** How to Create a Compelling Future	1
DAY 6	**The Driving Force:** Unleashing the Power of Your 6 Human Needs	1
DAY 7	**The Rapid Planning Method:** More Time for What Matters to You ▶ After You've Completed *Part II: Personal Power Classic*, go to *Part III: Get the Edge*	1

> *Nothing splendid has ever been achieved except by those who believe that something inside them was superior to circumstance.*
> **—Bruce Barton**

3

ANTHONY ROBBINS
ULTIMATE EDGE™

PART III
GET THE EDGE®

Transform Your Emotions, Health, Relationships & Finances: 7 Days to Tap Into the Tools & Resources That Get Results

DAY	SESSION TITLE	AUDIO CDs
DAY 1	**Results Workshop:** 7 Keys to Changing Anything in Your Life …Today!	2
DAY 2	**The Power of Relationships:** Passion, Connection & Love (Part 1)	1
DAY 3	**The Power of Relationships:** Passion, Connection & Love (Part 2)	1
DAY 4	**Pure Energy Live:** The Key to a Strong, Healthy & Vital Life	1
DAY 5	**The Power of Emotions:** Your Call to Action	1
DAY 6	**Financial Freedom:** Creating the Foundation for Lasting Wealth	1
DAY 7	**The Purpose of Life:** Finding Your Real Inner Drive ▶ After You've Completed *Part III: Get the Edge,* go back to complete Session 3 of *Part I: Inner Strength*	1

❝*The great end life is not knowledge but action.*❞
—Thomas Henry Huxley

TAKE ADVANTAGE OF YOUR FREE BONUSES!

PERSONAL JOURNAL

This personal journal is designed to help you get the most from your *Ultimate Edge* experience. Refer to it for a summary of each day's audio content. And after each session, use it to take immediate action on the day's assignment.

2 COUPONS

Take full advantage of your **$100 DISCOUNT COUPON** toward any Anthony Robbins' multi-day event as well as your **FREE 30-MINUTE** Coaching Strategy Session.

ONLINE PERSONAL PROFILE ($250 VALUE)

40-PAGE PERSONAL STRENGTHS PROFILE at no cost; **ONLINE** only.

POWER TALK!
AUDIO PROGRAM BONUS (3 VOLUMES)

ANTHONY ROBBINS' CONTENT AUDIO	ANTHONY ROBBINS' AUDIO INTERVIEW	BOOK SUMMARY	AUDIO CDs
Transformation: The Power of Expanded Identity	**Dr. Wayne Dyer**	**Jean Chatsky,** "Pay It Down! From Debt to Wealth on $10 a Day"	2
The Ultimate Resource	**William Strauss & Neal Howe**	**Viktor Frankl,** "Man's Search for Meaning"	3
Rules: The Source of Pain & Pleasure	**Dr. Robert B. Cialdini**	**Michael E. Gerber,** "E-Myth Revisited"	3

Anthony Robbins

Journal Notes

Anthony Robbins
Ultimate Edge™ Personal Journal

Table of Contents

Inner Strength®

Personal Power Classic®

Get The Edge®

"The life which is unexamined
is not worth living."
—Socrates

SESSION 1: DECISIONS & DESTINY
UNDERSTANDING AND DIRECTING THE
FORCES THAT SHAPE YOUR LIFE

To take our lives to the next level, we need to understand that the external world is not the driving force in who we become or what we choose to create for our lives. We all want to take control of the internal forces that shape the direction of our lives so that we may fully realize our emotional, physical, financial and spiritual potential. In the next few sessions we will learn the insights, tools, strategies and triggers that can change the quality of your life in a moment.

During the times in life where we get frustrated or overwhelmed or maybe even feel stuck, often there is something that snaps—a moment when everything changes. Regardless of what stage of life you may be in (if you are on a roll and want to continue to the next level, or if you are experiencing challenges you need to turn around), the *Ultimate Edge* helps you to cultivate the inner strength necessary to forge a path toward true meaning and happiness. Throughout the course of the program you're going to develop the triggers and recognize the patterns that enable you to take control and achieve success in all areas of your life.

Whether it's changing your body, turning around your finances or finding passion in your relationship, you will discover not motivation but inspiration for you to accomplish what you've always wanted and shape your own destiny.

> "The possibilities are numerous once we decide to act and not react."
> **—George Bernard Shaw**

SESSION 1: DECISIONS & DESTINY
UNDERSTANDING AND DIRECTING THE FORCES THAT SHAPE YOUR LIFE

The road to transformation begins with the foundation of the 3 Pillars of Progress.

FIRST PILLAR: GET FOCUSED AND CLEAR, AND MAKE IT COMPELLING

The first step is to **clarify the results you desire in your life.** What do you want most in the areas of life that are important to you? What is your definition of an extraordinary quality of life? What do you need to take your life to the next level?

Without a clear and compelling vision for what you want today, you won't be able to even find the target of lasting happiness, let alone hit it. Your chances of knowing what your bull's-eye looks like, however, depends on how honest you can be with yourself. When you've got a clear and compelling vision of what it is you want, it shifts your mind and emotions, giving you the impetus to shift your actions toward your goals.

SESSION 1: DECISIONS & DESTINY
UNDERSTANDING AND DIRECTING THE
FORCES THAT SHAPE YOUR LIFE

SECOND PILLAR: GET THE BEST TOOLS FOR RESULTS

Once you've defined your target, you need an effective and efficient game plan to hit it. In order to close the "gap" between where you are and where you want to be, you need a proven map, an effective mentor and training to drive you to take action. Armed with proven tools, high-quality skills, an effective coach to constantly measure your progress and an empowering community to hold you to a higher standard, there is no way that you won't get the results that you deserve!

THIRD PILLAR: GET INTEGRATED AND GET ALIGNED

However, sometimes tools are not enough: **you need to unlock what's blocking you and unleash your power.** Why is it that sometimes we know what to do, we have great motives for change, and yet we fail to follow through? Or we make changes in the moment, but they do not last long term? What's missing is a practical understanding of human psychology: why we do what we do and how to change it. **By understanding your personal blueprint—how you create meaning and emotion and what causes you to think, feel and behave the way you do—you can not only gain the answers to these questions but learn how to create lasting change and fulfillment.** Through the process of discovering, understanding and aligning your internal drives, you are able to channel them so that you naturally move in the direction you desire more—a direction that serves not only you but also all those you care about.

SESSION 1: DECISIONS & DESTINY
RESOURCES VS. RESOURCEFULNESS

The biggest illusion we have in life of why we can't achieve something is that we start to believe that we're lacking adequate resources. *I don't have enough money. I don't have enough time. I don't know the right people. I don't have the right training.* While any of these may in fact be true, there has certainly been something in your life where one or more of the above factors didn't stop you. You found a way. You may not have had the money, but you were creative enough to get it. You may not have had the education, but you found another way to learn a skill.

If the obstacle seems absolutely impenetrable but you're focused enough, will you find a way anyway? Of course you will, if you have enough determination, enough flexibility and enough creativity. The truth is resources are never the real problem. The real problem is a *lack of resourcefulness,* **and the ultimate resource is human emotion.** Human emotion is how we get the resources we need. We tend to forget this because we live and operate in a cognitively driven world, that is, we lean on our ability to figure things out. And if we reach a point where it seems like we can't figure out a solution, that's when the illusion of failure keeps us from reaching our goals. But in reality, if we feel strongly enough about something, no amount of time or perceived lack of resources would keep us from achieving what we want.

The mind needs fuel. It operates very differently when you're passionate about something than when you're frustrated, angry, bored or dejected. Your mind will wire itself differently when you're feeling excited, eager, enthusiastic, inspired or engaged in what you want to achieve, like there's a real purpose behind your goals. That passion expands into your thoughts, actions and the way you interact with people.

Change the fuel that drives the mind, and you change the experience of anything you're trying to accomplish. We're either unresourceful or resourceful based on the habit of emotions that we use most often. Once you realize that you are in control of the fuel that directs your thoughts and actions, the next step is to recognize the power of the decisions you make from moment to moment and throughout your life.

INNER STRENGTH®

SESSION 1: DECISIONS & DESTINY
TWO MASTER LESSONS OF LIFE

Gaining the ultimate edge in life requires mastering two skills: **the science of achievement and the art of fulfillment.**

Achievement—going from where you are to where you want to be—requires a plan, a specific strategy. You can achieve anything you desire simply by following certain laws. Whether you want to improve your financial outlook, enhance your relationships or sculpt your body into fantastic shape, following a set of scientific principles will guarantee results.

Fulfillment means experiencing tremendous joy in the process—so you feel not only the excitement of the pursuit but the enthusiasm and gratitude for the little things in life along the way.

If you're going to feel happy, alive, excited and passionate about life, you must understand that these lessons go hand in hand. Consider the very famous—although they achieve the heights of success, some never feel fulfilled despite the money, accolades and more. Remember, **success without fulfillment is the ultimate failure.**

SESSION 1: DECISIONS & DESTINY
THE POWER OF DECISION

Can you think about the areas in your life where you feel most fulfilled, be it your relationship, your career, your body or your family? The path to fulfillment is progressive—an ongoing journey or a project that engages your love, passion and time. More often than not, however, you can pinpoint a moment of significant change that inspired or triggered the actions that led to personal achievement. It is in these moments that you align and focus the power of your inner world to accomplish success and fulfillment in the external world.

The goal of the *Ultimate Edge* is to provide you with the knowledge and tools to create and take advantage of these moments of personal empowerment. Utilizing this power—this *emotional fitness*—to work against fear and doubt and overcome any obstacle allows you to become the architect of your own destiny instead of simply reacting to the forces in your environment.

> **The Ultimate Edge = Psychological Strength**
> Mental edge and focus that maximize who you are, what you're capable of and what you get to enjoy out of this life.

THE POWER OF DECISIONS

We are able to exercise this emotional fitness and psychological strength through action. Nothing changes without new action. It is also essential to remember that every action is parented by a decision. Before you take action, you **have to make a decision.** No matter how inconsequential a decision may appear to be, even the smallest decisive notion could change the outcome of your life. *It's in your moments of decision that your destiny is shaped.*

> **Decisions = Destiny**

Each day we're making new decisions and creating new actions, all fueled by the power of emotion. It is up to us to nurture the emotions that engender a level of positive activity and growth through consistent and focused decision-making. Some decisions may only have short-term impact, and others affect us far beyond what we could imagine in the moment. Either way, remember: decisions are shaping your life's destiny.

> **"**Once you make a decision, the universe conspires to make it happen.**"**
> **—Ralph Waldo Emerson**

SESSION 1: DECISIONS & DESTINY
THE THREE DECISIONS

There are three decisions you're making every moment of your life, either consciously or unconsciously. Developing the capacity to make the changes you want to make in life depends on your ability to become conscious of the decisions that you're making all of the time.

FIRST DECISION: WHAT ARE YOU GOING TO FOCUS ON?

Every moment of your life you have to decide what you're going to focus on. If you don't consciously choose where to point the lens, your brain just goes into the habit of what it usually focuses on. Most people focus on what they're afraid of, and whatever you focus on, you feel. So if you keep focusing on what you fear, you bring it to life. As you think about it, it becomes alive inside of you. On the other hand, if you focus on the potential in an event or situation, then opportunities begin to present themselves.

> *Wherever focus goes, energy flows.*

SECOND DECISION: WHAT DOES THIS MEAN?

The minute you focus on something, your mind has to come up with a meaning for it. From an evolutionary standpoint, the human nervous system *has* to know: is this going to mean pain or pleasure? Whatever meaning you give to an experience, then that experience becomes that meaning because you make it real in your body and mind. If you don't consciously choose what things mean, your old patterns show up. Come up with an empowering meaning, and you change how you'll feel.

> *What you feel begins with what you focus on and the meaning you give it.*

THIRD DECISION: WHAT AM I GOING TO DO?

Once you focus on something and give it a meaning, it produces an emotion. Those emotions filter what you do and trigger action, or even non-action.

If you're angry, are you going to do something different than if you're feeling grateful? If you're fearful, worried or stressed, are you going to do something different than if you feel determined, curious or playful?

> *Meaning powerfully affects what you're going to do.*

It all comes down to these three decisions. They're shaping your life moment to moment. If you take control of them, everything changes. You don't have to wait to be emotionally fit in order to start down the path that will lead to your ultimate edge. You have to decide to raise the standard of what you expect for yourself now. You have to *decide* that it's time to go to the next level.

ANTHONY ROBBINS

SESSION 1: DECISIONS & DESTINY
THE TWO FORCES THAT CONTROL OUR DECISIONS

There are two forces that influence every decision we make:

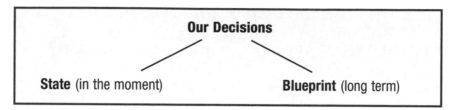

1. STATE

Ultimately, we want to feel states of empowerment, like confidence, certainty or adeptness, that will positively impact the quality of our decisions *most* of the time. Few people are in empowered states *all* of the time. But even "negative" states of emotion—frustration, anger, envy—can sometimes be useful to propel us to make changes. Being conscious of our moment-to-moment state gives us better control over how we feel, hence control over the quality of decisions we end up making.

2. BLUEPRINT

Our Blueprint is our *Model of the World*—a specific set of beliefs about how we're supposed to be, how life's supposed to be or how other people are supposed to treat us, which determines what we're even willing to consider doing or not doing. In short, our Blueprint will have a massive impact on the decisions we make both inthe short term and in the long term because it colors how we look at our lives

BLUEPRINT: A BRIEF INTRODUCTION

We experience happiness whenever our Life Conditions (what is actually happening with our career, body, relationships, finances, etc.) align with our Blueprint or Model of the World. Since there is no gap between our expectations and reality in this area, we are happy.

> **Life Conditions = Blueprint = Happiness**

But if there is an area of life that is causing you pain, it's because your Life Conditions do not match your Blueprint.

> **Life Conditions ≠ Blueprint = Pain**

INNER STRENGTH®

SESSION 1: DECISIONS & DESTINY
THE TWO FORCES THAT CONTROL OUR DECISIONS

Let's Take a Look at Your Life

1. What is an area of your life where you are really *happy*?

_____

_____

_____

_____

_____

2. Why are you *happy* in this area?

_____

_____

_____

_____

_____

3. What is an area of your life where you are not *happy*?

_____

_____

_____

_____

_____

4. Why are you *unhappy* in this area?

_____

_____

_____

_____

_____

We'll elaborate further on the important concept of Blueprint in the third session of *Inner Strength*.

Anthony Robbins

Journal Notes

SESSION 1: DECISIONS & DESTINY
THREE CHOICES

When we are unhappy and our Life Conditions do not match our Blueprint, we have three choices as to how we're going to handle the challenge:

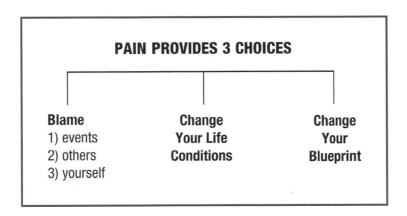

PAIN PROVIDES 3 CHOICES

Blame	Change	Change
1) events	Your Life	Your
2) others	Conditions	Blueprint
3) yourself		

FIRST CHOICE: BLAME

The first choice people have is to assign **blame,** and there are **three things you can blame:**

a) **Event.** There's a story, something that happened, behind why things are the way they are. However accurate the story may be, blaming an event is convenient because it helps preserve an identity designed to shield us from our true fears: fear of failure and fear of not being loved or accepted.

b) **Others.** *"I'm in this situation because this person ..."* Similarly, the story may be true, but it's convenient and gives you comfort in the moment. *"There's nothing wrong with me. It's this other person. There's nothing I need to change."*

c) **Yourself.** Most people think that this is being responsible, but blaming yourself will not make it better. There's a difference between responsibility and beating yourself up—between *"Here's a pattern that I've got to change"* and *"I'm not good enough."*

> **Blame is a choice that doesn't give you anything.**

SESSION 1: DECISIONS & DESTINY
THREE CHOICES

SECOND CHOICE: CHANGE YOUR LIFE CONDITIONS

Take a new action, something that will help you make significant progress. If you want to have happiness, you have to understand one thing: **progress = happiness.** If you feel like you're making progress in an area of your life, you will start to be pleased in that area. You start to get more focused and specific about what you want to change, and you build momentum toward the results you want. If, for example, you want to open your own business, find an achiever to mentor you. Get focused on why you want to make the change and commit to something new in your life.

THIRD CHOICE: CHANGE YOUR BLUEPRINT

Sometimes things are outside of your control, but you CAN control how you configure your rules about how things should be. Your happiness is going to be limited if you want success but aren't willing to ever be judged or want love but distrust the opposite sex. Sometimes adjusting your Blueprint means compromising some of your rules that are difficult for you and others to live up to or are simply impossible to fulfill.

When it comes to the three choices you face on how to handle a problem, the first choice isn't really a choice at all. Blame leaves you stuck, spinning your wheels with no options to change as you tell yourself, "There's nothing I can do about it because ..." We all use blame at times, but the quicker you can get out of it, the faster you'll be empowered to either change your life conditioning or change your perspective, both of which are real, tangible options that can instantly transform a relationship, your career, your finances or your *life*.

INNER STRENGTH®

SESSION 1: DECISIONS & DESTINY
MAKE A NEW CHOICE

EXERCISE: *Write What an Extraordinary Life Would Be Like for You Today ...*

Write a paragraph or two to answer this question: **What would your life be like if it was exactly the way you wanted it to be today?** In other words, **start with the ultimate end in mind.**

*If your life were extraordinary—**life on your terms**—what would that look like? How would you change? What would you enhance? Who would you spend more time with? What would you appreciate more? What would you do?*

_____

_____

_____

_____

_____

_____

_____

_____

_____

_____

_____

_____

_____

_____

_____

_____

_____

_____

_____

_____

_____

_____

_____

_____

_____

_____

ANTHONY ROBBINS

JOURNAL NOTES

SESSION 2: YOUR HOUR OF POWER
THE KEY TO PERSONAL
TRANSFORMATION AND RESULTS

There are two forces controlling every decision in our lives:

> • **State:** How you feel in any given moment.
> • **Blueprint:** Your structure of beliefs and values.

Remember, we'll further explore the dynamics of Blueprint later in ***Session Three of Inner Strength,*** but today we'll focus on the impact of **state.**

Hour of Power is designed to help you create rituals to condition empowering emotional states. Gaining the ultimate edge in life means experiencing the primary emotions you want regardless of life's events, not just attaining a life that works out every way you want it to. Sometimes, life rains on your parade, but you *can* control what it means to you. And when you control what it means to you, you have the edge, the ultimate advantage.

To make that happen, you must recapture what's missing—*time for yourself, time to heal mentally and emotionally* so that consistent space facilitates a shift in your habitual thoughts and feelings. You don't want to wait to attain a goal you've been looking to reach for a long time before you start feeling good about life. You want to direct the course of your life. Fulfillment is not an automatic result of success. Fulfillment is an emotion you must nurture to enhance your quality of life as you work toward your goals and beyond.

SESSION 2: YOUR HOUR OF POWER
TAKE STOCK OF YOUR EMOTIONS

W hich emotions do you feel on a regular basis? Make a list of all the emotions you consistently experience in an average week.

Empowering/Positive Emotions

_____

_____

_____

_____

_____

_____

_____

_____

_____

_____

_____

_____

_____

_____

_____

_____

_____

_____

_____

Disempowering/Painful Emotions

_____

_____

_____

_____

_____

_____

_____

_____

_____

_____

_____

_____

_____

_____

_____

_____

_____

_____

_____

> "Let's not forget that the little emotions are the great captains of our lives, and we obey them without realizing it."
> —**Vincent Van Gogh**

SESSION 2: YOUR HOUR OF POWER
THE THREE PATTERNS THAT CREATE
ANY EMOTION: THE TRIAD

Anything in life you want, you only want because of the feeling you think obtaining it will give you. But the truth is that you could have that feeling *right now*—simply by changing the following three patterns:

1. *Your Physiology*
   Emotion is created by motion. Whatever you're feeling right now is related to how you're using your body.

2. *Your Focus and Beliefs*
   Whatever you focus on is what you're going to feel whether it is true or not.

3. *Your Language*
   Questions: Thinking is nothing more than mentally asking and answering a series of questions. Eliminate any habitual questions that do not serve you (e.g., *"What's wrong with me?"*).

   Words: If you want to change your life, pay attention to the words you repeat to yourself. Certain words can change the way you feel: I think you're mistaken vs. I think you're wrong vs. I think you're lying.

   Incantations: When you repeat a phrase with enough emotional intensity, you start to believe it. Utilize the power of incantations by using the ones that support you the most.

SAMPLE INCANTATIONS

- Every day and in every way, I'm getting stronger and stronger.
- At last, at last, the past is past; I've broken free and won. And now it's time to love myself and really have some fun.
- With each and every breath I take, with each and every stride I make, I feel joy and love from deep inside me.
- Day by day I live my life with happiness and harmony. I share my gifts, my dreams, my heart, and love has set me free.

See page 37 for more Sample Incantations.

Tap Into Your Awareness
Get into the habit of evaluating your triad and conditioning yourself to experience the great emotions you want. What are you doing with your body? What are you focusing on or believing? What are you saying to yourself?

ANTHONY ROBBINS

JOURNAL NOTES

SESSION 2: YOUR HOUR OF POWER
YOUR DAILY HABIT FOR EXTRAORDINARY HEALTH AND HAPPINESS

Train yourself to jump out of bed immediately, with no hesitation, and start your day with movement.

PHASE 1: **Move and Breathe (5 Minutes)**

Keep your shoes beside the bed, and hit the ground running! Get up each day and physically move, going outside and starting with a walk to warm up your body and wake up your metabolism. Take several diaphragmatic breaths in the ratio: inhale for one count, hold for four counts and exhale for two counts.

Then, for the first five minutes of your walk, practice the pattern of "breathwalking." Inhale four times through your nose, exhale four times through your mouth and repeat continuously.

PHASE 2: **Get Grateful and Visualize (10 Minutes)**

Think about everything you're grateful for. Start with yourself, and include your family, friends, business associates and special moments in your life.

Visualize everything you want in your life as if you have already achieved it and you are grateful for it. Your brain can't tell the difference between something you vividly imagine and something you actually experience; whatever you focus on, you'll move toward.

Focus on what you want to create today. What do you want to make happen? What do you want to do, achieve or accomplish? See it happening the way you want it.

PHASE 3: **Use Incantations and Exercise (15–30 Minutes or More)**

Do your incantations out loud. Speaking engages your physiology and conditions the ideas into your mind.

Exercise and then celebrate!

YOUR ASSIGNMENT

STEP 1: Today, keep your eyes open for magic moments.

STEP 2: Tomorrow, first thing in the morning, start your day by doing your Hour of Power, 30 Minutes to Thrive or 15 Minutes to Fulfillment.

And remember, switch over to *Personal Power* and then *Get The Edge* before coming back to Session Three of *Inner Strength:* Your Personal Blueprint: The Ultimate Path to Pleasure or Pain.

Anthony Robbins

Journal Notes

Make sure you've listened to both *Personal Power Classic* and *Get The Edge* before moving on to this session!

SESSION 3: YOUR PERSONAL BLUEPRINT
THE ULTIMATE PATH TO PLEASURE OR PAIN

In the first session of *Inner Strength*, we discussed how the parent of action is our decisions. However, our decisions are controlled moment to moment by our state and by our Blueprint.

In Session 2 of *Inner Strength*, you learned how to get into the habit of evaluating your Triad and conditioning yourself to experience the emotions you want, maximizing an empowering state, hence empowering yourself to make better decisions and gain further control over the quality of your life.

Now that you've listened to *Personal Power* and *Get The Edge* and really started applying the strategies to begin that process of transformation, we turn back to what ultimately controls your thoughts, feelings and emotions: your Blueprint.

BLUEPRINT: A DEEPER LOOK

When any stimulus in life happens, how do you know if it's good or bad? How do you know if you should be angry or excited? How do you know if somebody just insulted you or teased you? When anything occurs, our minds have to decide how to respond. Whether we realize it or not, we're constantly feeding our minds a detailed outline for why we do the things we do.

There are people who have endured incredible pain and suffering but are happy and feel more alive than others who have not had those same challenges. Why? *Because they have a Blueprint that helps them find an empowering meaning behind anything that happens in life, even pain.* Becoming conscious of your Blueprint gives you ultimate control to head in the direction you want to go instead of being subconsciously guided by values, beliefs or rules that aren't serving you.

Sometimes, fine-tuning the schematics of your Blueprint may just require minor tweaks and adjustments to experience a truly fulfilling life. Other times, it may require going back to the drawing board altogether. But either way, you don't have to be a master architect of the mind in order to create a Blueprint that works for you through good times or bad. You just need to take a closer look at the forces that impact your Blueprint.

Session 3: Your Personal Blueprint
The Three Forces That Control Your Destiny

We judge whether or not we're being punished or rewarded by life's events based on our *needs, beliefs* and *habitual emotions.* The mind has to decipher: *Is this the end or is this the beginning? Should I be angry about this situation, or should I be excited?*

Unlocking the three forces that are moving you through life unconsciously, and redirecting these influences consciously, could change your life dramatically, eliminate pain, avoid unnecessary difficulties and give you more joy than you can imagine.

1. The Driving Force: The 6 Human Needs

Although we all have different Blueprints, different beliefs about different things, and can respond with different emotions to the same event, one thing we have in common is that we all have the same 6 Human Needs.

To review briefly from *Personal Power*, the 6 Human Needs are:

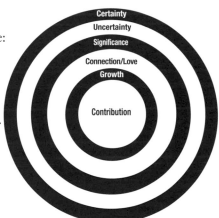

1. *Certainty:* to be comfortable, avoid pain and have some level of consistency.
2. *Uncertainty:* we need variety and change to feel alive.
3. *Significance:* the need to feel unique, special and important.
4. *Love and Connection:* to give and receive affection and support from others.
5. *Growth:* to become more, break through stagnation. We either grow or die.
6. *Contribution:* to give beyond ourselves.

Although every single person has the same 6 Human Needs, not everybody places the same importance on the same needs. If you put more emphasis on certainty, you're going to look at life completely differently than if you think the center of life is contribution.

Focusing more on any of the 6 Human Needs than the others is neither right nor wrong, but that focus will either create different opportunities and different problems, depending on where you are in your current Life Conditions. If you emphasize significance, giving it priority in your Blueprint may cause a conflict in the area of love and connection.

Additionally, the greater the difference is between your Life Conditions and your Blueprint, the greater the difference will be in your pleasure or satisfaction with the areas that you value most.

> *If you can pinpoint which needs you value most in practice—that is, which needs you strive to fulfill operationally in your everyday actions—and the needs you truly value most but may not consciously strive for, you can then close the gap and match your Blueprint with your Life Conditions.*

SESSION 3: YOUR PERSONAL BLUEPRINT
THE THREE FORCES THAT CONTROL YOUR DESTINY

2. THE GUIDING FORCE: MAP OF MEANING AND ACTION

Think of your belief system like a **map.** Your beliefs tell you how you get from where you are to where you want to be. Or you might think there's a **rule** that says, *"I've got to create the kind of relationship where there is always unconditional love,"* or *"I have to be aggressive, funny, giving,"* etc.

We have a map or rulebook in our unconscious mind that guides us in how to meet our needs and hit our targets. This becomes the way we think we need to be in order to get what we want.

> **To change your life, you must value one of your other needs more than the top two you value now.**

If one of your top two needs is love, learning to value another need more doesn't mean that you don't want love, or shouldn't want it. But if your focus is, *How can I GIVE love* (which can meet the needs for significance, growth or contribution) instead of *How do I GET love*, you literally change the direction and, ultimately, the destination of your relationship or your life.

3. THE FUEL OF CHOICE: HABITUAL EMOTIONS

Whatever it is you say you really want, whether you really get there or not is all going to come down to the *habit of emotion you get into most.* If your habit of emotion is frustration, feeling like a failure or feeling like you're not enough, that's what you'll unconsciously act out. However, if the habit of emotion you have is one of passion, determination, courage or playfulness, you've got a chance of getting the results you want. If you did the exercise in Session 2, then you examined the average week and put these emotions on a list on page 24.

Have you ever known someone who always finds a way to get upset or somebody who's not really funny—but they think they are—and you find yourself laughing anyway because they're having such a good time laughing at their own joke?

There's a center of gravity emotionally that you come back to on a regular basis—in your relationship, in your career or with your kids or partner. You can make a billion dollars, but if the primary emotion that you feel all day long is frustration, boredom or fear, your life will be one of frustration, boredom and fear. The emotions we live with day to day control the quality of our life more than anything else.

> **The quality of your life is the quality of your emotions.**

SESSION 3: YOUR PERSONAL BLUEPRINT
THE THREE P'S OF SUFFERING

Earlier we took a look at the formula for happiness, when Life Conditions equal your Blueprint. Likewise, when Life Conditions are not equal to your Blueprint, then there will be unhappiness.

We also know that when we experience unhappiness, we have two *real* choices: change our Life Conditions, or change our Blueprint. But sometimes that sense of unhappiness becomes so internalized that it feels like there's nothing you can do to change anything. That's when unhappiness reaches a peak and turns into *suffering*.

> **Suffering is when Life Conditions don't equal your Blueprint of how things should be, and you feel like you have no control to change it.**

Psychologist Martin E.P. Seligman, Ph.D., defined suffering as a form of learned helplessness. When you feel helpless—especially if you don't normally think of yourself as a helpless person—that feeling intensifies the suffering. The truth is there are no victims—there are only volunteers. However, the feeling of suffering comes from three aspects:

1. **You think the problem is *permanent*.** No problem is permanent. No matter how big the problem is, no matter how intense it seems, it's going to have an end. It may not end when you want, and it may not end the way you expected, but it will end. We do not always have control over life conditions, but the illusion that we can control everything except *meaning* is what makes us suffer.

2. **You think the problem is *pervasive*.** *"Because this relationship is messed up, my whole life is messed up. Because my finances are in ruin, everything is over."* No problem is pervasive. It just looks that way because you keep saying it's pervasive. Whatever the problem is, it doesn't have to affect everything. As long as you are alive, the problem is not permanent. Again, we go back to meaning.

3. **You think the problem is *personal*.** *"It's something wrong with me. There's a character defect in me. It's just the way I am."* When you think it's the way you are, you are not going to change it because you don't think you can. It's an identity issue.

No problem is permanent. No problem is pervasive. No problem is personal. It's just a matter of shifting your Blueprint. A Blueprint can change. Everyone has had some beliefs years ago that they would have fought for, which in hindsight would be almost an embarrassment to admit today.

Blueprints change all the time, and you can accelerate that change and eliminate suffering by getting clear about where your Blueprint is strong, where it's the essence of who you are versus something that you've practiced and adapted, where it's meeting your needs and where it's not. You can make empowering choices, change the conditions or change your Blueprint—so you are no longer controlled by something that you were previously unaware of.

INNER STRENGTH®

SESSION 3: YOUR PERSONAL BLUEPRINT
REVIEW

YOUR ASSIGNMENT

Turn back to your first assignment in Session 1 of *Inner Strength*, page 17, and review your answers on the areas of your life that you are happy and unhappy about. Now take a few minutes to dig further and open up that invisible part of you that controls your destiny by re-associating with what you wrote down in a deeper context, especially knowing what you know about your Blueprint.

1. What makes you happy?

_____

_____

_____

_____

2. Why does it make you happy?

_____

_____

_____

_____

3. What makes you unhappy?

_____

_____

_____

_____

4. Why does it make you unhappy?

_____

_____

_____

_____

SESSION 3: YOUR PERSONAL BLUEPRINT
WHAT'S YOUR LIFE ABOUT?

YOUR ASSIGNMENT

1. What's life ultimately about for you?

_____
_____
_____
_____
_____
_____
_____
_____
_____
_____
_____

2. What has to happen for life to be that way? What do you have to do? Do other people have to do something or be a certain way?

_____
_____
_____
_____
_____
_____
_____
_____
_____
_____
_____
_____

SESSION 3: YOUR PERSONAL BLUEPRINT
WHAT'S YOUR LIFE ABOUT?

3. Which one of the 6 Human Needs are you making most important in your life? What shift might you need to make to meet your needs?

_____

_____

_____

_____

_____

_____

4. Is this the best Blueprint you can come up with today? Why or why not?

_____

_____

_____

_____

_____

A. With all that you know about your life, what would be the more important need(s) to value?

_____

_____

_____

_____

_____

B. What's most important in life, and how will you get there?

_____

_____

_____

_____

_____

ANTHONY ROBBINS

JOURNAL NOTES

Bonus: Daily Magic
Your Ritual for Lasting Energy, Happiness and Success

Daily Magic is a unique audio program designed to guide you through your Hour of Power each day. Every day you will build and strengthen your mental, emotional and physical muscles so that you become the conqueror of the challenges in life and achieve the ultimate rewards.

STEP 1: Move and Breathe (5 Minutes)
STEP 2: Get Grateful and Visualize (120 Minutes)
STEP 3: Use Incantations and Exercise (15, 30 or 45 Minutes)

Be sure to celebrate!

MORE SAMPLE INCANTATIONS

- Every day and in every way, I'm feeling better and better.
- All I need is within me now.
- I love my life, and I am so blessed.
- Each day I live with more and more love, faith and positive expectations.
- I am so young, and I have my whole life ahead of me.
- I love myself, my mind, body, spirit and soul.
- I am so happy, and I can't stop smiling.
- Nothing tastes as good as fit feels.
- I am a lean, mean workout machine.

See page 25 for other Sample Incantations.

Or make up your own incantation:

_____

_____

_____

_____

_____

_____

*Remember, listening to your **Daily Magic** CD will support you in this process.*
Also be sure to activate your Free Coaching Strategy Session.

ANTHONY ROBBINS

JOURNAL NOTES

DAY 1—THE KEY TO PERSONAL POWER
HARNESSING THE POWER OF DECISION

Making decisions and using your Personal Power, which is your ability to take consistent action, change your life. This power is already within you and just needs to be awakened by igniting your desire and by showing yourself some simple systematic strategies on how to get greater results on a daily basis.

If you're dissatisfied with some area of your life right now, instead of getting frustrated, get exited. Because until you get dissatisfied, you won't do anything to really take your life to another level.

No matter what's happened in your past or how many times you've tried and failed, none of that matters because each moment is a fresh new opportunity.

THE ULTIMATE SUCCESS FORMULA

If you want to create success in your life, there are four steps:

1. Know your outcome.
2. Get yourself to take action by deciding to do so.
3. Notice what you're getting from your actions.
4. If what you're doing is not working, change your approach.

The biggest trap that keeps people from taking action is fear: fear of failure, fear of success, fear of rejection, fear of pain, fear of the unknown. The only way to deal with fear is to face it. Look it in the eye, and take action in spite of it.

It's not what we can do in life that makes the difference. It's what we *will* do. Often, we don't follow through because we don't know what we want, and when we do know, we're afraid to take action.

How long would you give the average baby to learn how to walk before you didn't let him try anymore?

Why wouldn't you apply the same formula to yourself?

"The past does not equal the future."
—Anthony Robbins

ANTHONY ROBBINS

DAY 1—THE KEY TO PERSONAL POWER
THE POWER OF MODELING

Success Leaves Clues

To save time and energy, use role models to accelerate the pace of your success:

1. Find someone who's already getting the results you want.
2. Find out what that person is doing.
3. Do the same things, and you'll get the same results.

It's impossible to fail as long as you learn something from what you do!

YOUR ASSIGNMENT

Never leave the site of setting a goal or making a decision without taking some action toward its attainment. That's how you create momentum and start to tap into the real driving force within you.

Complete the two steps on the following pages to take action and create momentum now.

> " I know of no more encouraging fact than the unquestionable ability of man to elevate his life by a conscious endeavor. "
> **—Henry David Thoreau**

DAY 1—THE KEY TO PERSONAL POWER
TAKING ACTION TO CHANGE YOUR LIFE

STEP 1: Make two decisions

What are two decisions you've been putting off which, when you make them now, will change your life?

_____

_____

_____

_____

_____

_____

_____

_____

_____

STEP 2: Take immediate action

What are three simple things you can do immediately that will be consistent with your two new decisions? Whom could you call? What could you commit to? What letter could you write? What could you do instead of your old behavior?

_____

_____

_____

_____

_____

_____

_____

_____

_____

_____

_____

_____

ANTHONY ROBBINS

JOURNAL NOTES

Day 2—Pain and Pleasure
The Controlling Forces That Direct Your Life

Ultimately, everything we do in our lives is driven by our fundamental need to avoid pain and our desire to gain pleasure; both are biologically driven and constitute a controlling force in our lives.

We will do far more to avoid pain than we will to gain pleasure. Pain is the greater motivator in the short term.

To get what you want in your life, you have to figure out what stops you. Whenever you procrastinate, it's because you think that taking action would be more painful than doing nothing or not taking action. Conversely, sometimes if you procrastinate for too long, it reverses on you! For example, if you keep putting something off (like a term paper or your taxes), you may get to a point the night before it's due where you start to think that not doing it will be more painful than doing it. And then all night long, you experience the pain of getting the job done.

You must learn to control the motivating forces of pain and pleasure.

How can you use this understanding? At any moment in time, you must realize that **your reality is based on whatever you focus on**. In other words, whatever you focus your attention on is what is most real to you.

> *Therefore, if you want to change your behavior, you must focus your attention on:*
> 1. How *not* changing your behavior will be more painful than changing it.
> 2. How changing it will bring you measurable and immediate pleasure.

If you are avoiding anything in your life or if you're sabotaging your success in any area, it's because you are experiencing approach/avoidance. You have a mixed set of associations about pain and pleasure. You think that by doing something (e.g. getting into a relationship), you will gain more pleasure, but at the same time, you think it might mean pain (e.g. the relationship might end). So as soon as you start to make progress, you sabotage it.

If you want to change this once and for all, **you have to decide right now that you control the focus of your mind**. If you're not following through, all you have to do is focus on "What's the pain I'm going to have if I *don't* do this?" instead of focusing on the pain you might experience from taking the action. You also have to focus on what pleasure you will experience when you do follow through. **You must change what you link pain and pleasure to in order to change your behavior**.

> ❝There's always a way—if you are committed.❞
> —**Anthony Robbins**

DAY 2—PAIN AND PLEASURE
UTILIZING PAIN AND PLEASURE TO CHANGE YOUR LIFE

YOUR ASSIGNMENT

Use pain and pleasure instead of letting pain and pleasure use you!

To take control of your life, you must take control of the force of decision. The power to change anything in your life is born the moment you make a real decision—which by definition is something that causes you to take immediate action. Take the following steps now.

STEP 1: Four new actions

What are four new actions you know you should take now?

_____

_____

_____

_____

_____

_____

_____

_____

_____

_____

_____

_____

_____

_____

_____

_____

_____

_____

_____

_____

_____

❝We accomplish things by directing our desires, not by ignoring them.**❞**
—Anonymous

DAY 2—PAIN AND PLEASURE
UTILIZING PAIN AND PLEASURE TO CHANGE YOUR LIFE

STEP 2: Pain you've associated with following through
What is the pain you've associated with these actions in the past?

_____

_____

_____

_____

_____

_____

_____

_____

_____

_____

_____

_____

STEP 3: Pleasure you've associated with not following through
What is the pleasure you took from not following through in the past?

_____

_____

_____

_____

_____

_____

_____

_____

_____

_____

_____

DAY 2—PAIN AND PLEASURE
UTILIZING PAIN AND PLEASURE TO CHANGE YOUR LIFE

STEP 4: Pain if you don't follow through
What will it cost you if you don't follow through now?

_____

_____

_____

_____

_____

_____

_____

_____

_____

_____

_____

STEP 5: Pleasure if you do follow through
What are the benefits you'll gain by taking action in each of these areas now? How will it enhance your life? How will it create greater joy, happiness, success, freedom or pride?

_____

_____

_____

_____

_____

_____

_____

_____

_____

_____

_____

_____

Day 3—The Power of Associations
The Key to Shaping Your Destiny

Specifically, what drives our lives is our neuro-associations—whatever pleasure or pain we associate or "link" to a situation in our nervous system is going to determine our behavior.

If we want to change our lives, we must change our neuro-associations:

1. The science you're learning about in this program is *Neuro-Associative Conditioning*® (NAC). This system will allow you to link massive pleasure to tasks you've been putting off but need to take action on today and to link pain to behaviors you're currently indulging in but need to stop—both of which will help you tap into the natural principles of your nervous system. The use of this program will give you a way to take direct control of all your behaviors and emotions in a way that simply requires the power of reinforcement, not discipline.

2. In this session, you learned to ask yourself, *"What are some of the negative associations I've made in the past that have kept me from taking the actions I need to take to achieve my ultimate desires?"*

3. Your neuro-associations control your level of motivation.

Every single action you take has an effect on your *destiny*. **If we study destiny, we find everything in life has four parts**:

1. Everything we think or do is a cause set in motion.
2. Every one of our thoughts and actions is going to have an effect or result in our lives.
3. Our results begin to "stack up" to take our lives in a particular direction.
4. For every direction, there is an ultimate destination or destiny.

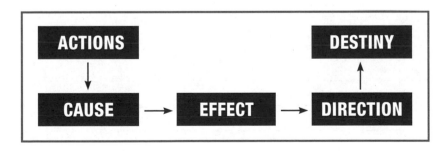

It's important for you now to begin to answer two questions: *What is your ultimate destiny? What do you want your life to be about?* While few people know precisely how their lives will turn out, we can certainly decide in advance the kind of person we want to become and how we want to live our lives. Having this "bigger picture" can pull us through some of the short-term tough times and keep things in perspective, allowing us to remain happy, fulfilled and driven to achieve our dreams.

ANTHONY ROBBINS

DAY 3—THE POWER OF ASSOCIATIONS
EMPOWERING VS. DISEMPOWERING NEURO-ASSOCIATIONS

YOUR ASSIGNMENT

Decide you will change these today. Simple awareness can be curative. It can break the pattern of allowing our unconscious conditioning to control us.

STEP 1: Three *empowering* neuro-associations from your past
What are three neuro-associations that you've made in the past that have positively shaped your destiny?

_____
_____
_____
_____
_____
_____
_____

STEP 2: Three *disempowering* neuro-associations from your past
What are three neuro-associations that you've made in the past that have disempowered you until now?

_____
_____
_____
_____
_____
_____
_____

"There is nothing either good or bad, but thinking makes it so.
—William Shakespeare

48

DAY 4—THE THREE STEPS TO LASTING CHANGE
THE SCIENCE OF NEURO-ASSOCIATIVE CONDITIONING®

To change your life, you must change your neuro-associations. Three things must be in place for you to make these changes and count on them to last. They are the three fundamentals of NAC:

1. Get leverage on yourself

To do this, three levels of responsibility are necessary—you must decide the following:

A. Something *must* change.
B. *I* must change it.
C. I *can* change it.

2. Interrupt your current pattern of association

You must scramble the old pattern of thinking and feeling. This is best done by using something unusual, such as making a radical change in what you say or how you move your body.

3. Condition a new empowering association

Install a new choice, and reinforce it until it is conditioned. **Any thought, emotion or behavior that is consistently reinforced will become a habit (a conditioned pattern).** Link pleasure to your new choice. Reward yourself emotionally for even small progress, and you will find yourself developing new patterns quickly.

BREAK YOUR PATTERN

Here is a bizarre, outrageous and effective way to get leverage and break your pattern:

Get a weight loss buddy, and promise him or her and a group of other friends that you will begin a strict regimen of healthy food and enjoyable exercise. Further commit to them that if you break your promise, you will eat a whole can of Alpo dog food.

The woman who shared this with me told me that she and her friend kept their cans in plain view at all times to remind them of their commitments. When they started to feel hunger pangs or considered skipping exercise, they'd pick up the can and read the label. Such appetizing ingredients as "horse meat chunks" helped them achieve their goals without a hitch!
(From *Giant Steps* ©1994 by Anthony Robbins)

> "We cannot think in one way and act in another . . ."
> **—Thomas Troward**

DAY 4—THE THREE STEPS TO LASTING CHANGE
THE SCIENCE OF NEURO-ASSOCIATIVE CONDITIONING®

For each or the four actions you listed yesterday, do the following.

STEP 1: Get leverage

Ten reasons why I must change now, and why I know I can do it:

_____

_____

_____

_____

_____

_____

_____

_____

_____

_____

STEP 2: Interrupt your own pattern

Four of five ways to get myself out of the limiting associations:

_____

_____

_____

_____

_____

_____

_____

_____

_____

_____

STEP 3: Condition yourself by rehearsing your new behavior

Give yourself a sense of accomplishment and exhilaration, pride, or joy each time you do this. Do it consistently and rapidly until each time you think of this new pattern, you feel good automatically.

> " What is necessary to change a person is to change his awareness of himself. "
> **—Abraham H. Maslow**

DAY 5—THE GOAL-SETTING WORKSHOP
HOW TO CREATE A COMPELLING FUTURE

Goals give you the ability to create your future in advance. They can make you grow, expand, develop your success and transform your life. If you already know some of your goals or you've done a goal-setting workshop in the past, here is a chance to do it again even more effectively.

Compelling goals contain two key components:

1. **Identify your goals:** *What do you want?*
   Something magical happens when you take generalized impulses of desire and start defining them more precisely.

2. **Identify your purpose:** *Why do you want it? What will it give you?*
   Reasons come first; answers come second. When you get a big enough reason to accomplish something, you can figure out how to do it.

YOUR ASSIGNMENT

As you listen to the real-time goal-setting workshop, follow my instructions and use the following pages to record your goals.

At the end of the session, take these three additional steps:

STEP 1: Keep your top nine goals and the reasons you are committed to achieving them in front of you on a consistent basis. Put them inside the cover of your journal or someplace where you will see them every day.

STEP 2: Never leave the site of setting a goal without taking some action toward its attainment. For each of your top nine goals, write down one action you can take immediately to make initial progress toward achieving it. Take that action today!

STEP 3: Take the *rocking chair test*: Imagine yourself much older, sitting in your rocking chair and looking back on your life, as if you had not achieved your goal; then imagine that you have achieved it. Experience the pain that would come from not doing it and the pleasure that would come from accomplishing your goal.

DAY 5—THE GOAL-SETTING WORKSHOP
HOW TO CREATE A COMPELLING FUTURE

Personal Development Goals

List your personal development goals. Next to each one, write down the time within which you are committed to accomplishing it (e.g., 1, 3, 5, 10, 20 years).

DAY 5—THE GOAL-SETTING WORKSHOP
HOW TO CREATE A COMPELLING FUTURE

Personal Development Goals

Identify your top three personal development goals. For each one, write a paragraph telling why you are absolutely committed to achieving this goal now.

DAY 5—THE GOAL-SETTING WORKSHOP
HOW TO CREATE A COMPELLING FUTURE

Things Goals

List your material goals. Next to each one, write down the time within which you are committed to attaining it (e.g., 1, 3, 5, 10, 20 years).

DAY 5—THE GOAL-SETTING WORKSHOP
HOW TO CREATE A COMPELLING FUTURE

Things Goals

Identify your top three material goals. For each one, write a paragraph telling why you are absolutely committed to attaining this goal now.

_____

_____

_____

_____

_____

_____

_____

_____

_____

_____

_____

_____

_____

_____

_____

_____

_____

_____

_____

_____

_____

_____

_____

_____

_____

_____

_____

_____

_____

ANTHONY ROBBINS

DAY 5—THE GOAL-SETTING WORKSHOP
HOW TO CREATE A COMPELLING FUTURE

Economic or Financial Goals

List your economic or financial goals. Next to each one, write down the time within which you are committed to accomplishing it (e.g., 1, 3, 5, 10, 20 years).

DAY 5—THE GOAL-SETTING WORKSHOP
HOW TO CREATE A COMPELLING FUTURE

Economic or Financial Goals

Identify your top three economic or financial goals. For each one, write a paragraph telling why you are absolutely committed to achieving this goal now.

_____

_____

_____

_____

_____

_____

_____

_____

_____

_____

_____

_____

_____

_____

_____

_____

_____

_____

_____

_____

_____

_____

_____

_____

_____

_____

_____

_____

ANTHONY ROBBINS

JOURNAL NOTES

Day 6—The Driving Force
Unleashing the Power of Your 6 Human Needs

All of us as human beings have different desires, but we are all driven by the same set of needs. Understanding the 6 Human Needs can allow you to turn on your driving force, discover all you're capable of and become truly fulfilled on a consistent basis.

The Four Classes of Experience

1. We usually think of a Class 1 experience as a "peak life experience." A Class 1 experience:
   - feels good
   - is good for you
   - is good for others
   - serves the greater good

2. Most people want to avoid Class 2 experiences, but mastering them brings us the most joy, growth and fulfillment. A Class 2 experience:
   - does not feel good
   - is good for you
   - is good for others
   - serves the greater good

3. Nonproductive Class 3 experiences provide immediate pleasure but eventually destroy our quality of life and give us ultimate pain. Drinking or eating to excess could fit into this category. A Class 3 experience:
   - feels good
   - is not good for you
   - is not good for others
   - does not serve the greater good

4. People often indulge in Class 4 experiences as a result of peer pressure, conditioning or old belief systems. Smoking cigarettes, for example, usually doesn't feel good the first time, yet many people continue to do it. A Class 4 experience:
   - does not feel good
   - is not good for you
   - is not good for others
   - does not serve the greater good

The secret to a happy and fulfilled life is learning to convert Class 2 experiences into Class 1—making the process of doing them feel good as well as be good.

DAY 6—THE DRIVING FORCE
UNLEASHING THE POWER OF YOUR 6 HUMAN NEEDS

The 6 Human Needs

All of us have the same problems because we all have the same 6 human needs. These needs are paradoxical—they seem to be in conflict with one another. Serious problems can arise when we choose destructive tools or vehicles to try to satisfy these needs. Instead, we can choose to establish new patterns of fulfilling our needs that will move us rapidly toward life mastery.

TO BE FULFILLED, WE MUST CONSISTENTLY MEET THESE 6 HUMAN NEEDS:

1. Certainty	2. Uncertainty
3. Significance	4. Love and Connection
5. Growth	6. Contribution

All human beings have the need for:

1. Certainty

For most people, certainty equals survival. As you heard in this session, when I was faced with the news of a pituitary tumor, it had a powerful effect on my level of certainty. We all need a sense of certainty that the roof will hold above our heads, that the floor will hold beneath our feet and that we can avoid pain and gain pleasure.

How do we meet the need for certainty? Some people try to achieve it by reaching for things that make them certain they can be comfortable: food, drugs, alcohol or cigarettes. Others find it by submersing themselves in their work or by trying to control everything around them—their environment or other people. These are usually Class 3 experiences (they may feel good for the moment but are not good for you, are not good for those around you and do not serve the greater good).

On the other hand, using your internal courage or faith to achieve certainty would be a Class 1 experience. When you're feeling courageous, when you're using your faith, you tend also to do those things that serve the greater good.

DAY 6—THE DRIVING FORCE
UNLEASHING THE POWER OF YOUR 6 HUMAN NEEDS

How do you try to get certainty in your life? *List some of the ways you try to be certain you can be comfortable, avoid pain and gain pleasure.*

_____

_____

_____

_____

_____

Here's the paradox, though. When you become totally certain, when things are completely predictable, you satiate this need and become b-o-r-e-d. And so while we want certainty, we simultaneously want a certain amount of . . .

2. Uncertainty/Variety

Everyone needs variety, a surprise, a challenge to feel fully alive and to experience fulfillment. With too much certainty, we're bored. Likewise, with too much variety, we become extremely fearful and concerned.

> People will violate their values to meet their needs.
> Choosing the wrong vehicle only leads to pain.

There's a delicate balance between these two needs that must be struck for us to feel truly fulfilled. We need a degree of certainty in our lives to appreciate the variety. Some people choose negative ways of getting variety, like using drugs or alcohol to change their emotional states or the way they feel. Others choose neutral vehicles, like watching movies. Still others use positive vehicles, like stimulating conversation and opportunities to learn.

How do you try to get variety in your life? *List some of the positive ways you try to create surprise, challenges and diversity in your life.*

_____

_____

_____

_____

_____

_____

_____

DAY 6—THE DRIVING FORCE
UNLEASHING THE POWER OF YOUR 6 HUMAN NEEDS

3. Significance

We all have a need for significance, the sense that we are unique in some way, that our lives have a special purpose or meaning. We can try to meet this need through destructive vehicles—for example, making ourselves unique by manufacturing a belief that we're better than everyone else or by developing extreme problems that set us apart. Medical science now shows that some people have even developed the subconscious ability to make themselves ill in order to gain the caring attention of others. This would clearly be a Class 4 experience.

Some people develop uniqueness by earning more money, having more "toys," going to school and achieving more degrees or dressing in a unique way and having a certain sense of style. Some choose to live lives of extraordinary service, a positive Class 1 experience that may feel like Class 2 at times.

How do you try to get significance in your life? *List some of the things you do that make you feel unique, needed, fulfilled or significant.*

_____

_____

_____

_____

_____

_____

_____

_____

_____

_____

_____

_____

_____

_____

_____

_____

We all need to feel unique. But paradoxically, to feel unique we have to separate ourselves from other people. If we feel totally unique, we feel different and separate, which violates our need for . . .

DAY 6—THE DRIVING FORCE
UNLEASHING THE POWER OF YOUR 6 HUMAN NEEDS

4. Love and Connection

All of us as human beings need to feel connected with ourselves as well as others with whom we can share our love.

To meet this need, you can join a group or a club that has a positive purpose. Some people join gangs, which have negative purposes but still provide that sense of connection. Some people feel immediate connection by aligning with their Creator and feeling like they're being guided. People will steal, take drugs or drink excessive amounts of alcohol to be part of a group and feel a sense of connection. Others will perform at extraordinary levels in order to be accepted, loved or connected to a high-performance team.

As with all 6 Human Needs, if you give consistently that which you wish to receive, you will tend to get it back from others.

How do you try to get love and connection in your life? *List some of the ways you try to feel connected to yourself, to others, to your Creator.*

_____

_____

_____

_____

_____

_____

_____

_____

_____

_____

_____

_____

_____

_____

These first four needs are the fundamental needs. The next two are the primary needs that must be met for you to feel totally fulfilled as a person.

DAY 6—THE DRIVING FORCE
UNLEASHING THE POWER OF YOUR SIX HUMAN NEEDS

5. Growth

Growth equals life. On this planet, everything that is alive is either growing or dying. It doesn't matter how much money you have, how many people acknowledge you or what you have achieved . . . unless you feel like you're growing, you will be unhappy and unfulfilled. But you must also be able to experience the euphoria of meaningful . . .

6. Contribution

We all have a deep need to go beyond ourselves and to live a life that serves the greater good. In the moments that we do this, we experience true joy and fulfillment. Contributing not only to others but to ourselves is a meaningful action, for we cannot give to others that which we do not have. A balance of contribution to oneself and to others, especially unselfish contribution, is the ultimate secret to the joy that so many people wish to have in their lives.

How do you try to get growth and contribution in your life? *List some of the things you do to obtain the feeling that you are growing and contributing—to yourself, to others, to the world at large.*

_____

_____

_____

_____

_____

_____

_____

_____

_____

_____

_____

_____

_____

_____

_____

_____

_____

Day 6—The Driving Force
Unleashing the Power of Your 6 Human Needs

If there is anything you love to do (and you could do for hours) that others find difficult, I can promise you it's because this activity meets all of your needs at a high level. If you find a few vehicles that meet all six of your needs, you'll find yourself full of drive and you'll know what to do to achieve your goals. And it all starts with awareness—you must become aware of why you're doing what you're doing and find a new pattern for fulfillment!

1. What's something you love to do, something you feel compelled to do, something that feels effortless for you? _____
   On a 0–10 scale, how much does this activity meet your need for:

Certainty	_____	Uncertainty	_____
Significance	_____	Love and Connection	_____
Growth	_____	Contribution	_____

2. What's something you hate to do, or try to avoid doing? _____
   On a 0–10 scale, how much does this activity meet your need for:

Certainty	_____	Uncertainty	_____
Significance	_____	Love and Connection	_____
Growth	_____	Contribution	_____

3. Write down something you don't like to do but have to do (a Class 2 experience that doesn't feel good but is good for you, is good for others and serves the greater good):

   _____

   Turn that activity into a Class 1 experience by finding ways to make sure it meets all six of your needs at a greater level.

   - **Certainty**: *What could I do or believe to make thinking about this activity feel not only comfortable but also pleasurable?* _____

   _____

   - **Uncertainty**: *How could I bring more variety to this task?* _____

   _____

   - **Significance**: *How can I appreciate how important this is?* _____

   _____

   - **Love and Connection**: *How can I feel more love while I'm doing this?* _____

   _____

   - **Growth and Contribution**: *How can I feel like I'm growing and contributing?* _____

   _____

ANTHONY ROBBINS

JOURNAL NOTES

DAY 7—THE RAPID PLANNING METHOD
THE POWER OF A RESULTS-FOCUSED LIFE

We live in a world where there are more demands placed on us now than at any other time in human history. We try to fill so many roles: ultimate father, ultimate mother, great lover, best friend to the world, community activist, spiritual being and total athlete. Some of us manage to cross off everything on our to-do lists—yet still feel unhappy and unfulfilled, as if we have no freedom, we have no life, we have no time. Oh, if only we had more time!

But what is time? Time is nothing but a feeling. If you want more time, you simply need to manage your feelings. Haven't you had periods in your life when time flew, when you had no stress, when everything seemed to flow effortlessly? And haven't you also had moments when time stood still, when every second was an eternity? It isn't time that causes stress; it's the feelings we generate about the subject of time.

What you focus on determines how you feel, and the questions you ask yourself control your focus. The Rapid Planning Method, or RPM, is a simple system of thinking that creates extraordinary results and an amazing level of personal fulfillment. RPM will help you do two things:

- Decide in advance what you want to focus on.
- Get yourself to focus every single day on what it will take for you to get the results you're really after.

RPM is a results-focused, purpose-driven, massive action plan that consists of three simple questions.

The Three Questions of RPM

Results: What do I really want? What is my outcome? What is the specific result I'm committed to achieving?

Purpose: Why do I really want it? What is my purpose?

MAP: What specific actions must I take to make this happen? What is my Massive Action Plan (MAP)?

> ❝ Success follows doing what you want to do.
> There is no other way to be successful. ❞
> —**Malcolm Forbes**

DAY 7—THE RAPID PLANNING METHOD
THE POWER OF CHUNKING

The Power of Chunking

The simplest chunking is in groups of three. Most phone numbers are chunked into three parts (area code, prefix, last four digits); so are Social Security numbers. Most people even have three names— first, middle, and last. It's much easier to remember three chunks than to remember 10 digits or a string of letters.

With the RPM system, you can easily chunk your to-do list from 12 items into three or four results or outcomes and create an RPM block: a result, a purpose and a set of action items.

> ### DEFINITION
> Chunking (chunk' ing v.) grouping information together into ideally sized pieces that can be used effectively to produce the result you want without stress or overwhelm.

In this session, you heard about Elvis, who decided to solve his weight problem by adding a 10-mile run to his to-do list. Elvis focused on this action item instead of establishing a clear picture of what he really wanted—to lose 20 pounds. There were many other ways Elvis could have achieved his outcome if he'd known what he really wanted. He needed to create an RPM block using these questions:

- What specific result am I committed to achieving?
- What's my purpose?
- What actions do I need to take?

Example RPM Plan

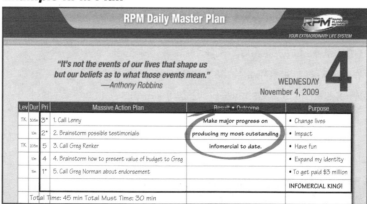

PERSONAL POWER CLASSIC®

DAY 7—THE RAPID PLANNING METHOD
CATEGORIES OF IMPROVEMENT

1. What are the six to eight most important areas of your life that you must make progress in every week?

2. What specific result do you want in each area in the next 90 days? The next 30 days? What do you want to make happen this week so you are making progress toward these results?

3. For each result, *why* must you make this happen? (Give yourself enough reasons to overcome the challenges that can show up later.)

> **SAMPLE AREAS**
> - My body
> - My family
> - My business or career
> - My spirituality, my relationship with my Creator
> - My friends and relationships
> - My finances

4. For each area, write at least the first two steps of your Massive Action Plan, or MAP. What two actions can you take? Whom do you need to call, what do you need to schedule and what can you do right away in each of these areas?

Area/Category _____

Results and Purpose

90 days _____

_____

_____

30 days _____

_____

This week _____

_____

Actions

1 _____

2 _____

3 _____

DAY 7—THE RAPID PLANNING METHOD
CATEGORIES OF IMPROVEMENT

Area/Category _____

Results and Purpose

90 days _____
_____
_____

30 days _____
_____
_____

This week _____
_____

Actions
1 _____
2 _____
3 _____

Area/Category _____

Results and Purpose

90 days _____
_____
_____

30 days _____
_____
_____

This week _____
_____

Actions
1 _____
2 _____
3 _____

DAY 7—THE RAPID PLANNING METHOD
CATEGORIES OF IMPROVEMENT

Area/Category _____

Results and Purpose

90 days _____
_____
_____

30 days _____
_____
_____

This week _____
_____

Actions
1 _____
2 _____
3 _____

Area/Category _____

Results and Purpose

90 days _____
_____
_____

30 days _____
_____
_____

This week _____
_____

Actions
1 _____
2 _____
3 _____

DAY 7—THE RAPID PLANNING METHOD
CATEGORIES OF IMPROVEMENT

Area/Category _____

Results and Purpose

90 days _____
_____
_____

30 days _____
_____
_____

This week _____
_____

Actions
1 _____
2 _____
3 _____

Area/Category _____

Results and Purpose

90 days _____
_____
_____

30 days _____
_____
_____

This week _____
_____

Actions
1 _____
2 _____

3 _____

Personal Power Classic®

Journal Notes

ANTHONY ROBBINS

JOURNAL NOTES

JOURNAL NOTES

DAY 1—RESULTS WORKSHOP
7 KEYS TO CHANGING ANYTHING IN YOUR LIFE TODAY

Happy, vibrant, successful people think and behave in certain ways. So do miserable and unfulfilled people. In other words, there are patterns of success and patterns of failure. The good news is, success leaves clues!

Why People Don't Change	The Antidote
1. They're out of practice.	• Raise your standards—The difference in people's lives is the difference in their standards. • Turn your "shoulds" into "musts"—When something is a must, you follow through. • Get unreasonable—Unreasonable people (like Nelson Mandela, Mother Teresa and Oprah Winfrey) rule the world. They do things others believe are impossible.
2. They rationalize, tell themselves stories, use softeners and lie to themselves.	• Develop self-honesty—Drop the story and tell yourself the truth. General Schwarzkopf teaches that nothing gets better until you admit something is wrong. • Understand the power of now—Tap into the power of momentum, and do something immediately. • Develop the habit of chunking—Start by tackling one manageable piece of a project: write one paragraph, make one phone call, walk for 10 minutes. • Stop using softeners—Making yourself feel better without actually changing anything trains you to accept mediocrity. Coach John Wooden taught his players that winning comes from telling yourself the truth and doing your own personal best.
3. They've had an ineffective strategy.	• Develop a strategy that works—You won't produce an extraordinary body by changing your diet alone. You need the right tools to get you there—a personal trainer, a support system, rituals that will ensure you stay on track.

DAY 1—RESULTS WORKSHOP
THE PRESSURE COOKER

There's one more reason people don't change—they get into a "pressure cooker."

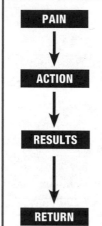

1. Pain Equals Drive
A person hits a threshold; the problem causes such a significant amount of pain that they feel pressure to take action to change it.

2. Drive Turns to Action
As a person takes action, they make progress toward eliminating some aspect of the problem (e.g., they lose 10 of their 40-pound weight loss goal), which lessens the intensity of the pain.

3. Actions Lead to Results
When the intensity of the problem is reduced, the drive to complete the change is lessened and motivation to completely resolve the problem is lost. With a lack of pain to drive the person any longer, gradually they return to the old behavior and . . .

4. Results Lead to Loss of Drive: Return to Past Actions/Return to the Problem
The problem remains.

People climb into the pressure cooker again and again! How can you avoid it?

The 7 Steps of Conscious Change

STEP 1: Get Disturbed

- *Be honest with yourself.* Don't use softeners or rationalizations; don't compare yourself with others to make yourself feel better.
- *Get associated to the problem.* If necessary, make it worse than it is to get yourself to take action. If you're not disturbed, you're not going to change.
- *Surround yourself with people who have what you want.* Seeing them will disturb you, and either you'll run back to your old friends to make yourself feel better or you'll join a new peer group. If you want to be good at tennis, play with somebody better than yourself.

EXERCISE: How do you rationalize?

What are the most common reasons you fail to do things? What stories do you tell yourself? List at least five rationalizations you use for not following through:

_____

_____

_____

_____

_____

_____

EXAMPLES
- I don't have time
- I'll do it tomorrow
- I'm tired
- It'll take too long
- It'll cost too much
- It's too far away

DAY 1—RESULTS WORKSHOP
THE POWER OF AN RPM PLAN

STEP 2: Make a Real Decision

What do successful people have in common? Successful people have an RPM for their lives.

R
P
M

Those who succeed in life have the answers to 3 questions:

1. **What is the specific result I am committed to achieving?** This is the **R**—the result they are after.

2. **Why do I want to do this? What is my purpose?**
   This is the **P**—the purpose. Once you decide, knowing your purpose—the "why"—will get you to follow through. Reasons come first; answers come second.

3. **What specific actions must I take to make this happen?**
   This is the **M**—the Massive Action Plan!

EXERCISE: Let's Get Honest

What are you unhappy about in your career, your business, yourself, your rationalizations? Write down some things that disturb you right now.

_____

_____

_____

_____

_____

_____

_____

_____

_____

_____

_____

_____

_____

_____

_____

_____

_____

DAY 1—RESULTS WORKSHOP
CREATING YOUR RPM PLAN

I'm disturbed about: _____

EXERCISE: Let's Get Honest (continued)

What are you committed to doing instead? Decide what new result you want; then write why (your purpose) you are committed to obtaining this result.

Result: *I am now committed to doing:*

_____

_____

_____

_____

_____

_____

_____

_____

_____

_____

Purpose: *I am committed to this because*:

_____

_____

_____

_____

_____

_____

_____

_____

_____

_____

DAY 1—RESULTS WORKSHOP
MASSIVE ACTION IS A CURE ALL

STEP 3: Create a Massive Action Plan

It's time to "draw the MAP." To make sure you follow through, come up with a list of actions that will absolutely produce results.

EXERCISE: Brainstorm Action Items

Choose one new result you are committed to achieving, and list all the things you could do to achieve it. Don't worry about making your list "perfect." Just brainstorm whatever comes to mind. Include little things that you can do immediately, and do them *now*. Never leave the site of setting a goal without doing something toward its achievement. Send an e-mail, make a phone call, book a meeting, buy a book, etc.

_____

_____

_____

_____

_____

_____

_____

_____

_____

_____

_____

_____

_____

_____

_____

_____

_____

_____

_____

_____

_____

Now asterisk (*) the three to five "must items" you can and must do to achieve your goal.

" A mighty flame follows a tiny spark. "
—**Dante**

DAY 1—RESULTS WORKSHOP
THE POWER OF PURPOSE

EXERCISE: Brainstorm Action Items (continued)

Using language that excites you, refine the wording of your result, list a few reasons why you want to take this action (your purpose) and then commit to the actions by giving each one a deadline.

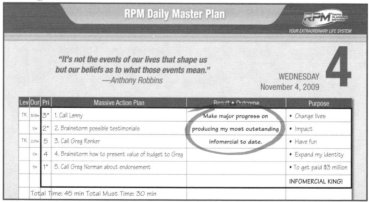

Example RPM Plan

> "It is not enough to be busy. The question is, what are we busy about."
> **—Henry David Thoreau**

DAY 1—RESULTS WORKSHOP
BELIEFS: THE POWER TO DESTROY/THE POWER TO CREATE

STEP 4: **Change Your Limiting Beliefs**
A belief is nothing more than a feeling of absolute certainty about what something means. Beliefs control our behavior. They can be unconscious or conscious, and they often stem from things we've heard or seen, felt a lot of emotion about and then repeated to ourselves again and again until we felt certain.

- John McCormack's empowering belief in himself turned him from a policeman risking his life to "save someone else's $27" into a millionaire and Entrepreneur of the Year. After losing it all, his limiting belief nearly caused him to give up . . . until a new empowering belief turned him around again.

- The young lady who believed exercise was painful, expensive and not really necessary adopted empowering new beliefs that exercise allows her to give more, that she's worth it and that it's fun.

- Josh's old beliefs caused him to gain 110 pounds; his new beliefs helped him lose the weight and make exercising and eating well part of his daily routine.

EXERCISE: **Old Beliefs, New Beliefs**
Write down all the *old beliefs* that have kept you from following through on your goal in the past.

_____

_____

_____

_____

_____

Write down the *new beliefs* that will empower you from this point forward.

_____

_____

_____

_____

_____

ANTHONY ROBBINS

JOURNAL NOTES

DAY 1—RESULTS WORKSHOP
SCORING YOUR LIFE

STEP 5: Set Yourself Up to Win

- *Reward yourself.* When learning something new, most people don't do it perfectly the first time. To win the game of life, you've got to reward yourself for doing things approximately right in the beginning.

- *Score the experience.* Do things that add emotional intensity and make the process more enjoyable along the way. If you're working out, you can listen to music, work out with a buddy, pray while you exercise, etc. Choose things that meet all of your 6 Human Needs.

- *Take advantage of NET time.* Increase the value of your time by doing several things at once. It takes NET . . . no extra time!

- *Measure your progress.* You'll be excited about your results if you measure your progress. Set yourself up to win by measuring in more than one way. For example, if you only measure the pounds you lose, there may be days when you don't see results. Measure anything that can give you growth.

> ### 6 HUMAN NEEDS
>
> All human beings are driven by six needs. No matter what task is at hand, you'll enjoy the process and accelerate your results by making your actions meet your needs for:
>
> 1. Certainty
> 2. Uncertainty
> 3. Significance
> 4. Love and Connection
> 5. Growth
> 6. Contribution

EXERCISE: Enhance the Experience

Come up with two or three ideas that can help you look forward to doing the things that will get your result. What can you focus on, pay attention to, notice, appreciate or enjoy that will enhance the experience?

_____

_____

_____

_____

_____

_____

_____

_____

_____

DAY 1—RESULTS WORKSHOP
THE POWER OF ACTION

STEP 6: Take Massive Action

- There is no time like the present! Never leave the site of setting a goal without doing something toward its attainment. Do something while you're inspired, while you're "in state." The more massive the action, the more committed you will be to achieving the result.

- The power of incantations—you can't just get rid of a negative belief; you have to replace it. Try incanting your new beliefs, saying them again and again, changing the emphasis and changing your state. By changing the emotion, you change the impact you feel, and you begin to condition yourself for even more action.

- Massive action creates momentum. You don't have to do a thousand things; you just have to do something.

EXERCISE: Little Action, Big Action

What are two actions you can take immediately to get yourself going?

Little action (e.g., make a phone call, send an e-mail)

_____

_____

Big action (something that takes time, energy, money or effort)

_____

_____

STEP 7: The Seventh Power

When you care how people feel about you, you make them your peers and you give them power to influence the way you think. Tap into the Seventh Power—the power of environment. Choose a peer group with a high standard, utilize a coach and immerse yourself in an environment that reinforces you for your wins and challenges you to greater heights.

> **REMEMBER THE MARINE CORPS GENERAL . . .**
>
> Most people's lives are a direct reflection of the expectations of their peer group.

YOUR ASSIGNMENT

Do the little action and big action you wrote down. Do them right away, and be sure to acknowledge yourself when you get them done!

DAY 2—THE POWER OF RELATIONSHIPS (PART 1)
PASSION, CONNECTION AND LOVE

There are two universal laws of life: anything that doesn't grow dies, and anything that fails to contribute is eliminated. These laws hold true for everything in life, especially for relationships.

Extraordinary relationships—not merely good or excellent, but truly legendary ones—are those in which the participants continually grow and contribute to themselves, the relationship and each other.

IDENTIFY THE GAP BETWEEN WHERE YOU ARE AND WHERE YOU WANT TO BE

1. *Where are you?*
   If you're in a relationship, you
   - want more from it
   - want out of it
   - are immobilized

   If you're not in a relationship
   - you want one but don't have one; you fear being hurt
   - you don't want one; you've been hurt before

2. *Where do you want to be?*
   Visualize your ideal relationship. What would it look like? What would you talk about, laugh about, share, learn together? How would you make love, surprise and contribute to each other?

The Purpose of Relationships

Relationships exist to magnify the human experience. Which emotions are you magnifying–negative ones or positive ones?

THE SECRET TO HANDLING UPSETS

When we associate pain to a relationship, we're responding to the past. These are independent events. Remember *this* is not *that*.

Instead of assuming the worst, become a master of meaning. What else could be happening in this situation? What else could this mean? Most of the time, it's not about you.

Remember Dr. Sigmund Freud's wise words—"Sometimes a cigar is just a cigar!"

DAY 2—THE POWER OF RELATIONSHIPS (PART 1)
THE ULTIMATE LOVE OF YOUR LIFE

The quality of your relationships is in direct proportion to the amount of yourself you are able to share. Sharing produces a synergy where one plus one equals more than two.

- *Go to a relationship to give, not to get.*
  Measuring and remembering who gives more is a surefire way to kill a relationship. When driven by rules instead of love, relationships begin to die.

- *Keep your rules to a minimum.*
  Too many rules can destroy a relationship. Upsets occur easily when you have too many ways to feel bad.

- *Help your partner meet his or her needs.*
  Although we go about meeting them in different ways, we all have the same six needs. Passionate relationships occur when both partners feel that their needs are met.

- *Understand the importance of awareness and acceptance.*
  Be aware that all human beings share the same two primary fears: that they are not enough and that they won't be loved. Primary fears are triggered anytime you feel like you're not being seen as significant enough or you fear the loss of love. If you're starting to react, ask yourself, "What's really triggering this fear? Am I responding to the present or the past? What else could this mean?"

How to Create an Extraordinary Relationship

1. *Learn to Love Yourself*
   You can't give to other people what you haven't learned to give yourself. Write at least 10 things you can do to show how much you love yourself (Do my Hour of Power, 30 Minutes to Thrive or 15 Minutes to Fulfillment; acknowledge myself for being great; write myself a love letter; go to places I love).

_____

_____

_____

_____

_____

_____

_____

_____

_____

_____

DAY 2—THE POWER OF RELATIONSHIPS (PART 1)
SELECTION: THE KEY TO OUTSTANDING RELATIONSHIPS

2. *Select the Qualities You Need in a Relationship*
Relationships last when both people have the same or complementary natures. Follow the example set by business leaders, and consider three things in evaluating a potential relationship (business or personal):

- **Can they do the job?** Can they be your partner?
- **Will they do the job?** The answer will be yes if the job or relationship meets their personal goals and reinforces their nature.
- **Are they the right fit in terms of values?** In a personal relationship, is there a match in terms of goals, values, sensuality or sexuality?

CAN DO
(Knowledge, habits, skills)

WILL DO
(Natural behavior rewarded by demands of the relationship. Relationship moved toward personal goals.)

TEAM FIT
(Do you share one of the top two needs with the other persons?)

Organizing Principles

- The most important part of selection is to first become the kind of person you want to attract in your relationship.
- It is unlikely a person's nature is going to change. Know who you are in a relationship with.
- If you are in a relationship with the right person for you and you are still having challenges, you can re-ignite the passion.

DAY 2—THE POWER OF RELATIONSHIPS (PART 1)
ASSESSING WHERE YOU ARE

YOUR ASSIGNMENT

1. Where are you in your intimate relationship? Which scenario best describes the current state of your intimate relationship?

_____

_____

    1. The love and passion are good, but I want more.
    2. Love is there, but not enough passion.
    3. Love and passion are lacking—we're more like friends.
    4. I'm planning my escape.
    5. I'm not in an intimate relationship, but I want to be in one.
    6. I'm not in an intimate relationship, and I don't want to be in one.

_____

_____

_____

_____

_____

Wherever you are, be honest. Remember, honesty will bring you clarity.

2. Now, whether you are in a relationship or not, describe what your ideal relationship would be like. What would you do together? How would you have fun? What would it be like to be physically, emotionally and spiritually intimate the way you truly want to be? What do you/would you have in common? How would you ideally raise children? Even if you are already in a relationship and it's great, what more do you want?

_____

_____

_____

_____

_____

Begin closing the gap by describing where you are now and where you want to be.

DAY 3—THE POWER OF RELATIONSHIPS (PART 2)
DESIGN YOUR IDEAL MATE

The first step in finding and attracting your ideal mate is defining what you want in that person. If you don't know what you're looking for, your ideal mate could walk right by you and you might not even notice him or her! By clarifying precisely what you want and reviewing your list each day, you will literally program your unconscious to help you find your ideal person.

EXERCISE: Design Your Ideal Mate

The Ideal Mate

Describe your ideal mate's traits, habits, qualities, appearance—everything you can think of that would be important to you.

The Mate from Hell

If you have a hard time coming up with your "wish list," start by defining "the mate from hell." Write about the person you couldn't stand to be with. What traits would they have? What qualities could you not stand?

_____	_____
_____	_____
_____	_____
_____	_____
_____	_____
_____	_____
_____	_____
_____	_____
_____	_____
_____	_____
_____	_____
_____	_____
_____	_____

Note: If you are already in a relationship that you want to make better, this process will help you discover each other, renew the reverence in your relationship and meet each other's needs at a much deeper level.

DAY 3—THE POWER OF RELATIONSHIPS (PART 2)
ATTRACT YOUR IDEAL MATE

EXERCISE: Design Your Ideal Mate (continued)

What Kind of Person Would You Have to Be to Attract Such a Mate?

You need to become the kind of person you would like to find. Describe the values, characteristics, conduct and habits you would need in order to deserve the mate you just described.

_____

_____

_____

SCOTT'S LIST
I need to be:
• Kind
• Loving
• Flexible
• An open communicator
• Driven by values
• Intelligent
• Nurturing

Asterisk (*) the "musts."

DAY 3—THE POWER OF RELATIONSHIPS (PART 2)
DEAL WITH CHALLENGES

Closing the Gap

To close the gap between where you are and where you want to be, you've got to know where you really are. If you're already in a relationship, go back to the "must" items on your lists from Steps 1 and 2. On a 0–10 scale, first rate your partner and then rate yourself on how well those musts are being met.

If you're not in a relationship, score yourself alone. Go back to your must items from Step 2, and rate yourself on a 0–10 scale. How close are you to being the person who will attract the kind of person you want?

How to Deal with the Inevitable Challenges That Will Arise

Challenges show up in every relationship. If the same ones seem to keep popping up and if they seem overwhelming, it may be that your natures are completely different and not complementary or that you don't share the same values.

Running from a relationship is not the answer. Anywhere you go, you take yourself with you! Honesty and clear communication are the only solutions.

- Have an honest conversation with your partner about ways to meet both your needs and theirs.
- Make yourself stronger and better, give more, focus on their needs.

Sometimes you have to make the hardest decision of all about the relationship. Get clear on what's best for you and the other person.

> "There is no remedy for love but to love more."
> —**Henry David Thoreau**

DAY 3—THE POWER OF RELATIONSHIPS (PART 2)
TAKE YOUR RELATIONSHIP TO THE NEXT LEVEL

STEP 1: First Learn to Love Yourself

For the next seven days, take two minutes each morning to look in the mirror and repeat, "I love you [your name], I love you [your name] . . ." Tell yourself the specific reasons you love yourself.

Write down some of those reasons here.

_____

_____

_____

_____

_____

_____

_____

STEP 2: If you're in a relationship, make an action plan for taking it to the next level.

Make a list of things you can do to enhance your relationship. Or if you truly are not matched in your natures, your values and your goals, get really clear about that, have an honest conversation and make some decisions. Make a game plan for what you are going to do.

_____

_____

_____

_____

_____

_____

_____

DAY 3—THE POWER OF RELATIONSHIPS (PART 2)
TAKE YOUR RELATIONSHIP TO THE NEXT LEVEL

Step 3: If you're single, make a marketing plan for attracting your ideal mate.

Where do you need to spend your time? Whom do you need to talk to? Create a plan for the next 30 days.

_____

_____

_____

_____

_____

_____

_____

_____

_____

_____

_____

_____

_____

_____

_____

_____

_____

_____

_____

_____

_____

_____

_____

_____

_____

> "We are all born for love. It is the principle of existence, and its only real end."
> —**Benjamin Disraeli**

JOURNAL NOTES

DAY 4—PURE ENERGY LIVE!
THE KEY TO A STRONG, HEALTHY AND VITAL LIFE

Relationships, finances, emotions, your career . . . none of these matter if you don't have your health. To avoid ending up as "the richest person in the graveyard," make your health an absolute priority.

Don't let anyone convince you to give this responsibility to "experts." You must be your own authority. Model people who not only have studied the subject but have consistently used it to achieve the results you desire. With a few simple changes, you can give yourself the gifts of explosive energy, improved immune function and weight loss.

The Truth about Germs and Illness

Ten people can be exposed to the same germ, but not all of them become ill. Why? Because germs are not the source of disease. Contact with a specific germ is not an absolute guarantee of contracting disease. Several other factors are involved:

- The amount of stress or emotion in your life
- Your genetic tendencies
- The things you do to keep your body in balance
- The pollution level of your environment (your body)
- Your philosophies about health

The Acid-Alkaline Balancing Act

Our bodies are driven by electrical impulses in a complex electromagnetic system. This system requires a delicate balance between the levels of acid and alkalinity. You can easily test this balance by measuring your pH level; ideal blood pH is 7.36.

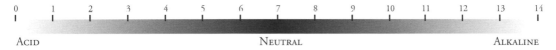

Acid in the system disrupts the balance, causing red blood cells to stick together, weaken and die. When this happens, more acid is released into the bloodstream, causing a vicious and deadly cycle of pollution. The body tries to compensate by calling upon its alkaline reserves, but eventually these are depleted and acid wreaks havoc, burning through your arteries. Again, the body tries to compensate by lining the artery walls with cholesterol . . . another deadly solution!

> " The greatest mistake a man can make is to sacrifice health for any other advantage. "
> —**Arthur Schopenhauer**

[*Note: We recommend that you consult with a healthcare professional before beginning any nutritional program.*]

DAY 4—PURE ENERGY LIVE!
THE CYCLE OF IMBALANCE

Alkalize and Energize

The key to maintaining balance is found in two simple steps:

STEP 1: Alkalize

Alkalizing breaks the cycle of excess acid. It's the difference between life and death, between losing weight and keeping it on.

STEP 2: Energize

Your body operates on a subtle electromagnetic current. Your brain, your heart and all of your organs emit fields of electrical impulses. Foods provide value only when they can be converted into the elements necessary for this chemistry to take place. *Energizing* means avoiding foods that take away more energy than they provide.

SUBSTANCE	MHz
Big Mac	5
Chocolate Cake	1–3
Vitamins	10–30
Raw Almonds	40–50
Green Vegetables	70–90
Wheat Grass	70–90
A Rose	70–90
Green Drink	250–350
Your Liver	55–60
Your Colon	58–63
Your Stomach	58–65
Top of Your Head	60–70
Your Brain	72–78
A Tumor	30

How You Get Out of Balance

1. Your environment is *disturbed* by something

- Emotions—negative emotions, thoughts, words and actions have a tremendous impact on your bloodstream.
- Polluted environment—smog in the air makes you acidic.
- Acid diet—animal proteins, cooked oils, sugar and refined carbohydrates are all sources of acid. *Sugar equals acid and acid equals glue.*
- Radiation—no one really knows what impact constant exposure to things like computer screens may have, but excess radiation could easily disturb the delicate acid/alkaline balance.

2. Cells become *disorganized*

- When cells are disturbed, they become disorganized in an attempt to deal with or adapt to the new (disturbed) environment. They weaken, die or mutate.

3. As cells attempt to adapt, the environment is *compromised*

- Ruptured or dead cells give off excess acid. The new environment becomes a breeding ground for bacteria, yeast, fungus and mold.

4. The environment becomes *polluted*

- Bacteria, yeast, fungus and other creatures feed on your energy stores and excrete acid waste, causing even more pollution, more disturbance, more disorganization and more acids.

5. You develop what most people think of as *debilitating disease or aging*

- The truth is, it's an acid problem that begins with disturbance.

DAY 4—PURE ENERGY LIVE!
THE CYCLE OF BALANCE

The Three-Step Cycle of Regaining Balance

1. Cleanse your system, ideally for 7–10 days (or a minimum of 3–4 days)
- You don't need a blood test to know you've built up some toxicity and acid through your lifestyle until now. The best way to cleanse is to superhydrate your system with plenty of fluids that are alkaline in nature. Green drinks, such as wheat grass or our **Inner Balance** green drink product, will provide an instant boost to your alkalinity.

2. Interrupt destructive patterns that don't serve you
- Identify and break your destructive patterns. Stop indulging in negative emotions or eating acidic foods.

3. Provide your body with the core nutrients it really needs
- Water
- Oxygen/breathing
- Vitamins & minerals
- Live alkaline foods
- Exercise

Regaining Balance: Stories of Success

- *Hypercholesterol Study:* The National Institutes of Health followed an entire family whose cholesterol levels were over 450. After switching to an alkaline diet, one woman lost 50 pounds and lowered her cholesterol by 190 points in just six weeks.
- *Seeing Is Believing:* I saw my own blood cells go from torn and leaking to healthy and intact. I felt better than ever and saw the proof under the microscope with my own eyes.
- *Sean's Wish:* Remember Sean? Within 12 months, he went from being fragile and breakable to doing pushups and sporting a "six-pack" of abdominal muscles.

YOUR ASSIGNMENT

Everything in life shifts when you put yourself back in balance. Take control of your body with this simple three-step challenge. For the next 10 days:

STEP 1: Cleanse your system
STEP 2: Interrupt destructive patterns that don't serve you
STEP 3: Provide your body with its vital needs

Never leave the site of setting a goal without doing something toward its attainment. If you're ready to take your life to the highest level of energy possible, make sure you follow these steps and do something right now.

DAY 4—PURE ENERGY LIVE!
CREATING A HEALTHY, VITAL LIFE

STEP 1: Cleanse your system

Start cleansing right away by drinking plenty of water. Another way to do it is with high-alkaline green drinks, like wheat grass or *Anthony Robbins' Inner Balance™ Pure Energy Greens.* For more information about this and other *Inner Balance™* products, all designed by Harvard nutritionist Dr. Stacey Bell, call: **877-GO-4-GREEN (877-464-4733) or do an online health evaluation at www.TonyRobbins.com/InnerBalance**

> **HOW MUCH WATER IS ENOUGH?**
>
> Drink half your body weight in ounces every day. If you weigh 200 pounds, drink 100 ounces of water.

STEP 2: Interrupt destructive patterns that don't serve you

Write down at least three destructive patterns in which you've been engaging. Come up with one or two ways to interrupt each pattern the next time it arises.

Destructive Pattern
Example: I often get angry.

Pattern Interrupts
When I begin to feel angry, I will take five deep breaths and list at least three things I'm grateful for in my life.

_____ _____
_____ _____
_____ _____
_____ _____
_____ _____
_____ _____
_____ _____

STEP 3: Provide your body with its vital needs

Write a paragraph or two describing why you are now committed to providing your body with the things it needs. What will it give you? What has not doing this up until now caused you to miss out on or lose in your life?

_____
_____
_____
_____
_____
_____

DAY 5—THE POWER OF EMOTIONS
YOUR CALL TO ACTION

Frustration, anger, resentment, depression—compare these emotions to joy, passion, contentment, excitement and ecstasy! Our lives are defined by the emotions we feel on a daily basis. What we do is not based on our ability, our talent or our skills it's based on how we feel. Most of us live our lives in reaction to our environment. Our emotions are like the ocean—some days they're a brewing storm; other days they're as calm as they can be. This session is about taking control of the most important and powerful part of your life: your emotions.

Emotions are signals calling us to action. Often, the emotions that seem the most painful may be telling us we need to make changes. If we heed these signals, we can utilize them to change the quality of our experience and our lives immediately.

Where do emotions come from? Whether we give ourselves positive, negative or neutral feelings is determined by the rules we have and the meanings or interpretations we attach to events in our lives. What we feel is based not on our experience but on our interpretation of the experience. Remember . . . *You are always in control of how you feel. Nothing controls you but you*.

Exercise: Hope vs. Certainty

1. Think about something you'd like to have happen in the future and hope it will happen. Close your eyes and notice how it feels to hope. Do you see two different possibilities—having it work out and not work out?

2. Open your eyes, shake your body out a little and get rid of that hoping feeling. Now close your eyes and think about this same thing you'd like to have happen, but this time expect it to happen. Notice how it feels and how this is different from hoping.

3. Open your eyes. What was the difference? *You just controlled your emotions!*

> " There can be no transforming of darkness into light
> and of apathy into movement without emotion. "
> —**Carl Jung**

DAY 5—THE POWER OF EMOTIONS
THE 10 ACTION SIGNALS

If You Feel . . .	The Message is . . .
1. *Uncomfortable*	• Change your state, clarify what you want and take action in that direction.
2. *Fearful*	• Get prepared; get ready to do something.
3. *Hurt*	• An expectation is not being met, and you have a feeling of loss. Change your behavior or your way of communicating your needs.
4. *Angry*	• An important rule has been violated. Let the person know that your standard may not be the same as theirs, but you need their help.
5. *Frustrated*	• You need to change your approach to achieve your goal.
6. *Disappointed*	• Your expectation may not be appropriate for the situation at hand.
7. *Guilty or Regretful*	• You violated one of your own standards. You must ensure you won't violate it again.
8. *Inadequate*	• You need to improve what you're doing or change your criteria; your rules may be too hard to meet.
9. *Overloaded, Overwhelmed, Hopeless or Depressed*	• You need to prioritize. List the things you want to accomplish in order of priority, then take action with the first item on your list.
10. *Lonely*	• You need connection with people.

> "Nothing in life has any meaning except the meaning you give it. If you don't like the way you're feeling, change the meaning."
> —**Anthony Robbins**

DAY 5—THE POWER OF EMOTIONS
MASTERING YOUR EMOTIONS

Six Steps to Mastering Your Emotions
How do most people handle their emotions? They avoid them endure them or use them to compete with other people. There's a fourth way, a better way, and you can do it in six simple steps —learn from your emotions and utilize them!

1. Identify the emotion and appreciate the message:
  • It's saying you have to change something.

2. Clarify:
  • What is this emotion trying to tell me? What message is it offering?
  • Do I need to change my perception (the meaning) or my procedures (my communication or my behavior)?

3. Get curious and ask questions:
  • How do I really want to feel? As soon as you identify what you want to feel, you're moving in the direction you want to go.
  • What would I have to believe in order to feel that way now?
  • What am I willing to do to make it the way I want it?
  • What's great about this, or what can I learn from this?

4. Get confident:
  • Recall a specific time when you felt this emotion before and somehow got over it.
  • Remembering a time when you were able to deal with the emotion will reassure you that you can deal with it now.

5. Get certain:
  Imagine coming up with different ways of handling this emotion. If one doesn't work, try another. Rehearse until you feel confident.

6. Get excited and take action!
  Do something right away that shows you can handle this emotion. Express your emotion in a way that reinforces what you've rehearsed in your mind and changes the way you feel.

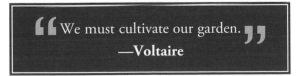

> **"**We must cultivate our garden.**"**
> **—Voltaire**

DAY 5—THE POWER OF EMOTIONS
THE 10 EMOTIONS OF POWER

The 10 Emotions of Power

The best way to get yourself to do something is to put yourself in an emotional state where that behavior becomes automatic. For example, the easiest way to have close relationships and do the things that make you feel close to other people is to cultivate the emotion of being loving and warm. Here are 10 quick emotions to plant in your life on a daily basis. If you cultivate these emotions and focus on feeling them every day, you will plant the seeds of greatness in your life.

1. *Love and Warmth*

2. *Appreciation and Gratitude*

3. *Curiosity*

4. *Excitement and Passion*

5. *Determination*

6. *Flexibility*

7. *Confidence*

8. *Cheerfulness*

9. *Vitality*

10. *Contribution*

DAY 5—THE POWER OF EMOTIONS
TRANSFORM YOUR EMOTIONS

Let's start using the six steps and the 10 action signals we've learned in this session.

STEP 1: For the next two days, notice any negative or disempowering feelings that come up, and apply the six-step process. Record your progress below.

Negative emotion: _____

_____

How I handled it: _____

_____

_____

_____

_____

Negative emotion: _____

_____

How I handled it: _____

_____

_____

_____

Negative emotion: _____

_____

How I handled it: _____

_____

SIX STEPS TO MASTERING YOUR EMOTIONS

1. Identify the emotion and appreciate the message
2. Clarify: What is it trying to tell me? Do I need to change my perception or my procedures?
3. Get curious:
   - How do I really want to feel?
   - What would I have to believe in order to feel that way now?
   - What am I willing to do to make it the way I want it?
   - What can I learn from this?
4. Get confident: I've handled things like this before.
5. Get certain: Rehearse dealing with it in the future.
6. Get excited and *take action!*

_____

_____

DAY 5—THE POWER OF EMOTIONS
UTILIZE YOUR ACTION SIGNALS

STEP 2: Make a list of all the things you can do to make yourself feel good.

_____

_____

_____

_____

_____

_____

_____

_____

_____

_____

_____

_____

_____

_____

_____

> Most people have only a few ways to feel good. Expand your list and include things you can do at any moment in time, no matter where you are, like . . .
>
> - Taking a deep refreshing breath
> - Singing your favorite song
> - Feeling grateful for love in your life

STEP 3: For each of the 10 action signals you learned in this session, develop a new belief that will help you avoid feeling these emotions

Disempowering Emotion	_My New Belief_
Examples: Overwhelm, Disappointment	"This too shall pass" or "The best is yet to come" or "There's always a way if I'm committed."

1. Uncomfortable _____   _____
2. Fear _____   _____
3. Hurt_____   _____
4. Anger _____   _____
5. Frustration_____   _____
6. Disappointment_____   _____
7. Guilt or Regret_____   _____
8. Inadequacy _____   _____
9. Overload, Overwhelm, Hopelessness or Depression _____   _____
10. Loneliness _____   _____

DAY 6—YOUR WAY TO FINANCIAL FREEDOM
THE POWER OF COMPOUNDING

Obtaining the financial freedom and abundance you deserve is easy. The secret to getting beyond scarcity is to start beyond it by feeling a sense of abundance *right now* and living your life as if you already were financially independent.

Does This Really Work?

You bet it does! In this session, I shared my story of going from scarcity to abundance and back again to illustrate a few key points I learned along the way:

1. **Make it a must**

   Give yourself a compelling future that makes it impossible for you to fail. My must for financial independence was the birth of my son and my desire to give him an extraordinary quality of life.

2. **Get hungry**

   Stop blaming everyone else. Set your goals, make them a must and commit to making the necessary changes *now*.

3. **Add value to other people's lives**

   Remember, your income is in direct proportion to your contribution.

4. **Don't be a victim of the "tall poppy syndrome"**

   Other people may want to chop you down to their size, but don't let that happen!

The Power of Compounding

Compounding occurs when you invest money and allow it to continuously reinvest itself. With this strategy, you'll realize explosive growth beyond your wildest imagination.

Examples:

- **In an 18-hole golf game, if you bet just 10 cents on the first hole and double your bet every hole thereafter, the last hole will be worth $13,107.20.** *No matter how little you start with, you must start now!* If you wait until the third hole to begin, betting on 15 holes instead of 18, the total comes to only $1,600.
- Saving $150 a month ($5 a day) at a 15% annual return for 30 years yields $1,051,000.
- Saving $250 a month in that same period of time produces $7.8 million.
- Investing $100 a month at your child's birth at a 15% rate of return results in $110,000 when the child turns 19. Leave it alone, and it grows to $9.6 million when he or she is age 50, $32.9 million at age 60, and $158 million at age 70!
- UPS deliveryman Ted Johnson never made more than $30,000 a year but left a legacy of more than $70 million!

Statistics show you're going to live a long time. What are you going to do when you get there? Handling your finances is critical, and compounding is the ticket, so start investing *now*. If you're not willing to take a dime out of a dollar today, you won't be anymore likely to take a hundred thousand out of a million later.

DAY 6—YOUR WAY TO FINANCIAL FREEDOM
THE MOST IMPORTANT INVESTMENT DECISION
YOU WILL EVER MAKE

The Value of Stocks

- **Long-term dependability**
Since World War II, the best investment through time has been the stock market, delivering a 12% rate of compounded return for nearly 50 years.

- **Short-term flexibility**
Buying and selling stocks is fast and easy. It's much faster, for example, than selling a piece of real estate.

Sir John Templeton's Strategy: "Three Bucket" Asset Allocation

Decide what percentage of your income to invest, and allocate it into each of the following areas in a proportion that meets your needs and satisfies your risk tolerance. By determining your asset allocation in advance and sticking to your plan, you'll avoid the temptation of spur-of-the-moment decisions.

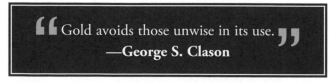

1. Security Bucket

This bucket is for low-risk investments such as fixed income (treasury bills, corporate bonds, money market accounts) and equity (insurance policies, your home). The growth rate on these investments seems slow at first but compounds over time. What goes into this bucket should stay here—allow the profits to be reinvested.

2. Growth Bucket

This bucket is for higher-risk investments with more potential for growth, such as mutual funds, collectibles, real estate and stocks. Reinvest one-third of the profits in your security bucket, one-third in your growth bucket and one-third in your dream bucket.

3. Dream Bucket

This is the place to have some fun and save for the things you want in life. Whether it be a boat, a yacht, a vacation home or a sports team, this bucket lets you start building toward your dreams and making them come true.

Pay Yourself First!

Here's the best-kept secret to painless investing: Never see the money! Decide how much you want to invest, and have it deducted directly from your paycheck.

> **❝**Gold avoids those unwise in its use.**❞**
> **—George S. Clason**

DAY 6—YOUR WAY TO FINANCIAL FREEDOM
TWELVE STRATEGIES FOR ACHIEVING WEALTH

Why People Fail to Become Wealthy: 12 Financial Traps to Avoid

1. They never define what wealth means to them.
2. They make wealth a moving target.
3. They define wealth in ways that make it impossible to achieve.
4. They never even start.
5. They never make wealth an absolute must.
6. They don't have a realistic plan.
7. They fail to follow through.
8. They make "experts" responsible for their decisions.
9. When faced with major challenges, they give up.
10. They fail to conduct life as if it was a business.
11. They allow other people's emotions to affect the implementation of their plan.
12. They never get quality coaching.

How to Be Wealthy Right Now

This part is easy! Just do the exact opposite of the 12 financial traps:

1. Define what wealth means to you, exactly what will it take for you to feel wealthy.
2. Lock that definition firmly in place. Don't keep raising the bar.
3. Make sure your definition is achievable.
4. Create a plan that is achievable.
5. Make it a must for you by listing the reasons you must be wealthy.
6. Finalize your plan and work out the details.
7. Follow through on your plan by taking immediate action toward its attainment.
8. Make yourself responsible. Let experts coach you, but don't abdicate your responsibility.
9. Don't give up when the going gets tough.
10. Make your life a business, and expect a year-end profit.
11. Don't let other people's emotions control or cause you to deviate from your asset allocation.
12. Get good coaching.

Finally, remember that real wealth comes from an abundance in all areas: mental, emotional, physical and spiritual. The real key to unlocking wealth is just one thing . . . gratitude. The moment you feel grateful is the moment you feel rich.

> **❝** The way to achieve success is first to have a definite, clear practical ideal—a goal, an objective. Second, have the necessary means to achieve your ends—wisdom, money, materials, and methods. Third, adjust your means to that end. **❞**
> —**Aristotle**

DAY 6—YOUR WAY TO FINANCIAL FREEDOM
DECIDE, DEDUCT AND DARE TO DREAM

STEP 1: Decide how you're going to allocate your assets.

I'm going to invest _____% of my income.

I'm going to split my investments in this ratio (for example, 50/50 or 60/40):

Security Bucket: _____%

Growth Bucket: _____%

STEP 2: Make it a must for you. Write a paragraph or two about why you must be wealthy and what it will do for you, your family, your life. What will it give you? Who will you be? What will you do with your wealth?

_____

_____

_____

DAY 6—YOUR WAY TO FINANCIAL FREEDOM
CREATE YOUR FINANCIAL PLAN

STEP 3: Start making your plan. Write down the steps you must take to begin or improve your investing strategy.

_____

_____

_____

_____

_____

_____

_____

_____

EXAMPLE:
• Open a money market account
• Call accounting and start my payroll deduction
• Start researching stockbrokers
• Call Robbins Research and get a great coach!

_____

_____

_____

STEP 4: Never leave the scene of a decision without taking some action. Choose two of the items you listed in Step 3, and do them today. Make a note of what you did:

_____

_____

_____

_____

_____

_____

_____

_____

_____

_____

_____

_____

ANTHONY ROBBINS

JOURNAL NOTES

DAY 7—THE PURPOSE OF LIFE
FINDING YOUR REAL INNER DRIVE

Everything on earth has a purpose—and that includes you! Your purpose in life provides you with an inner drive that, once you tap into it, can give you immense fulfillment and unlimited joy.

Your Purpose in Life

- does not change
- is eternal
- is available to you each and every moment

Three Decisions Shape Your Life

Everything you do has a consequence. What ultimately shapes your life, though, are the decisions you make. You *can* have the life you deserve, where all your consequences are positive ones. How? By making these three decisions:

1. **Decide what to focus on**
   What you focus on determines how you think, feel, contribute. Choose an empowering focus in every situation.
2. **Decide what things mean**
   Meaning is something *you* determine. You cannot control events, but you can control what events mean to you.
3. **Decide what you will do when something happens**
   Remember, God's delays are not God's denials . . . unless you give up.

Discover the Sources of Pain

Whatever drives you shapes your life. Human beings are primarily driven by two things: the need to avoid pain and the need to gain pleasure. Pain can be useful, like when a child learns to stay away from a hot stove, or pain can be destructive, as it was for the woman who believed marriage equaled death.

Why am I feeling this pain?

1. What *unique* thing is happening when I feel this pain?
2. What *recent* thing happens about the same time I feel the pain?
3. What *consistent* factor is present when I experience the pain?

If you're experiencing pain in any area of your life, these three questions can help you discover the source, decide whether it's helping or hurting you and give you the information you need to create a deeper meaning.

Day 7—The Purpose of Life
The Power of a Compelling Future

How Will You Know Your Life's Purpose? When You Decide What It Is!

- According to the Massachusetts Department of Health, Education and Welfare, the most important risk factor in dying of your first heart attack is job dissatisfaction. Make sure you have a deeper meaning for your life than "I'm on that grindstone again!"

- Victor Frankl, a Nazi concentration camp survivor and author of *Man's Search for Meaning*, found his purpose in his future. He vowed that somehow he would survive, share his story and make sure that nothing like the Holocaust could ever happen again.

- Near the end of his life, actor Michael Landon discovered a profound truth. In reminding people to live life to the fullest, every minute of every day, he developed a compelling purpose for his final days.

Your Purpose in Life Is Up to You

Are you being efficient or effective? Being efficient means doing things right. Being effective means doing the right things.

Why Some People Don't Win the Game of Life

So many people feel like they can't win the game of life. Why? For these seven reasons:

1. They don't know the purpose of the game.
2. Even though they don't know the purpose, they have rules for themselves and everyone else about how the game must be played.
3. Their rules are in conflict.
4. Even when they play by the rules, they don't always win.
5. Sometimes they get rewarded for breaking the rules.
6. They have to work with other people who all have the wrong rules.
7. They think it's a life-and-death game, putting so much fear and pressure on themselves that they never truly live.

> " This is the true joy in life, the being used for a purpose recognized by yourself as a mighty one: the being a force of nature instead of a feverish, selfish little quad of ailments and grievances complaining that the world will not devote itself to making you happy. "
> —**George Bernard Shaw**

DAY 7—THE PURPOSE OF LIFE
HOW TO WIN THE GAME OF LIFE

Seven Strategies Used by Winners

1. They decide the purpose of the game.
2. They have fewer rules about how to be happy.
3. Their rules are consistent.
4. They give themselves pleasure whenever they win.
5. They give themselves short bursts of pain if they violate their sense of purpose in life.
6. They know that everybody has different rules. Their relationships succeed because they try to understand the other person's rules.
7. They don't take life too seriously.

Lose a Dream and Find Your Destiny

No matter what happens, you must find an empowering meaning. Ask yourself, "How can I use this?" Often in life, when you look back on your worst situations, they turn out to be your best—if you are willing to trust that they happened for a reason. Look for the benefits, and you will find them.

Don't wait for that glorious moment when you save someone's life. Start saving a life today by enjoying the one you have. Find your purpose in something simple, like Cecil did: love people, love animals, love beings and make the world a little bit better just by being nice.

SOMETIMES NOT GETTING YOUR DREAM GIVES YOU YOUR DESTINY

Doc Graham, in the film *Field of Dreams*, got to play baseball for only five minutes.
To him it wasn't a disaster . . . but being a doctor for only five minutes would have been.

Why do angels fly?
Because they take themselves lightly.

DAY 7—THE PURPOSE OF LIFE
DISCOVER YOUR LIFE'S PURPOSE

Life is about two things: being and doing. Ultimately, your destiny is about who you become and what you do. To discover a greater sense of meaning for your life, follow these three steps and start discovering your life's purpose.

STEP 1: **Remember what you wanted to be when you "grew up," and remember the times when you felt like you were really "on a roll."**

  1. With your eyes closed, remember when you were five, six, seven years old. What did you want to be when you grew up? Why did you want to be that? What feeling did you hope it would give you?

  _____

  _____

  _____

  _____

  _____

  _____

  _____

> **WHEN YOU WERE A KID**
>
> • What did you want to do?
> • Why did you want to do that?
> • What feelings were you hoping to get from that?
> • Who were your role models?
>
> I wanted to be an archaeologist, a police artist, a rock star. Today I dig for the truth and hang out with bands like Aerosmith!

  2. Think of something else you wanted to be when you were growing up. Why did you want to be that? What feeling did you hope it would give you?

  _____

  _____

  _____

  _____

  _____

  _____

  _____

  _____

  _____

DAY 7—THE PURPOSE OF LIFE
DISCOVER YOUR LIFE'S PURPOSE

3. Think of a third thing you wanted to be. Again, why did you want to be that? What feeling did you hope it would give you?

_____

_____

_____

_____

_____

_____

4. Now, with your eyes closed again, think about a time when you were really on a roll, where things flowed effortlessly. What were you doing, feeling, experiencing?

_____

_____

_____

_____

_____

_____

5. Think of another time you were on a roll, where you felt, "This is what life's about." What was happening? What were you doing? How were you feeling? Were other people involved? How were you being, and what were you doing? Capture not only the idea but the feeling as well.

_____

_____

_____

_____

_____

_____

6. Think of a third time when you felt incredible. Notice what you were doing, creating, sharing, feeling.

_____

_____

_____

_____

_____

DAY 7—THE PURPOSE OF LIFE
DISCOVER YOUR LIFE'S PURPOSE

STEP 2: Write your purpose.

Write a simple phrase, a sentence or two. It doesn't have to be perfect the first time. Keep brainstorming, writing several until you find the one that feels right.

Your purpose statement must:

1. Be stated in the positive
2. Be brief
3. Include "emotionally charged" words
4. Tell how you're going to be, what you're going to do
5. Include yourself and others
6. Be achievable in your lifetime
7. Be able to be experienced every day
8. Make you happy . . . really happy!

> **EXAMPLE**
> The purpose of my life is to be fun, happy and grateful, to enjoy my life and share my love with others.

The purpose of my life is to:

_____

_____

_____

_____

_____

STEP 3: For the next month, keep your purpose statement in front of you.

Put a copy in the system you use for managing your life, and hang another copy on a nearby wall. As you look at it each day, think about how you can live your purpose even more.

I can live my purpose even more by:

_____

_____

_____

_____

_____

> **"** Nothing can resist the human will that will stake even its existence on its stated purpose. **"**
> —**Benjamin Disraeli**

Remember to go back and complete Your Final Intergration: Session 3 of *Part I: Inner Strength.*

THE JOURNEY CONTINUES ...

The *Ultimate Edge* starts with taking control of the one thing that every one of us can do in an instant: choose what we are going to give our attention to, making a commitment to measurable improvement in the areas we want to change. But if you're going to make incalculable progress toward your goals, an immersion experience multiplies the intensity of the tools included in this product.

So be sure to take advantage of the $100 discount included in this product for *Unleash The Power Within ("UPW"),* our signature 3½-day weekend event that helps you:

- Learn the secret to peak performance.
- Convert the energy of fear into constant momentum that becomes an unstoppable force.
- Experience the thrill of storming across a bed of burning hot coals.
  (You don't have to, but you'll want to!)
- Master the powerful skills of rapport and influence to maximize your effectiveness
  as a parent, partner, businessperson and leader.
- Learn how to boost your energy, health and vitality.

UPW comes with a money back guarantee if it doesn't do everything you want, but you've got to stay for at least half of the program. Imagine what four days of total focus will do to internalize the strategies you've learned so far. It'll change your life forever! For more information, call **800.466.7111** or visit **www.tonyrobbins.com.**

The second aspect of total immersion is individual attention–someone to hold you accountable and help you with a personalized plan to follow through—so be sure to take advantage of your free coaching strategy session with an Anthony Robbins trained coach. Call **800-431-4267** to schedule your session. (for international dialing, call **001.858.535.9900**).

And don't forget to fill out your **online personal profile** to better understand the areas you are the strongest in, and those you need to focus on for constant and never ending improvement. By consistently practicing the tools provided in this program, you will have conditioned your mind, body, emotions and spirit to soar—you will deal with problems that show up in radically different ways. In fact, they aren't problems but rather challenges for you. And more importantly, you'll be excited to connect with people; you'll be excited about your projects. You will affect people around you in a different way because you will have an extraordinary psychology. Once your intentions are aligned with your thoughts and actions, nothing can hold you back.

Don't forget to check out *Transformation: The Power of Expanded Identity*, the first of your three bonus *PowerTalk!* programs.

ANTHONY ROBBINS

JOURNAL NOTES

LIVE EVENTS, PRODUCTS AND RESULTS COACHING

MASTERY UNIVERSITY®
DISCOVER A LIFE OF LASTING SUCCESS AND TRUE FULFILLMENT

WHAT IS MASTERY UNIVERSITY?

To take our lives to the next level, it's important to realize the same pattern of thinking that has gotten us to where we are now will not get us to where we want to be in life.

Mastery University is the most advanced system you'll find for revolutionizing the many aspects of life—whether it's your health, relationships, finances, emotions, time or career. The 13½-day program is divided into a series of three distinct sessions that are attended over a 12- to 24-month period. You'll also have access to a series of live and online coaching sessions designed to accelerate and reinforce the knowledge you will acquire.

Of the thousands who participate every year, many share personal success stories made possible because of this powerful program.

There has never been a better time to create an extraordinary life than now.

Anthony Robbins, the foremost authority on the psychology of leadership, negotiation and peak performance, created Mastery University for leaders committed to finding resources for expanding and improving the quality of their lives.

"I was successful, but I had no balance in my life. Tony helped me shift my values. I now live a life by my own design, with explosive energy and razor-sharp focus. I have an amazing relationship, and my companies will reach $20 million in revenue this year!"

—BILL LYONS
President and CEO, LEI Financial
San Diego, California

For More Information, Call 800.397.6329

TAKE THE EXTRAORDINARY POWER OF ANTHONY ROBBINS' TECHNOLOGIES WITH YOU WHEREVER YOU GO!

THE TIME OF YOUR LIFE®
16-Day Program to Change Your Life

More Time for What Really Matters to You—This unique 10-day step-by-step audio program is designed to help you master the Rapid Planning Method (RPM). Take control of your time, and your life, as you massively increase your productivity, efficiency and fulfillment.

Includes: 16 audio CDs, custom manual, summary cards, RPM sample form and Time Plus™, a 19-page personalized online time assessment.

RPM® LIFE MANAGEMENT SYSTEM®
Your Extraordinary Life System

The Anthony Robbins Rapid Planning Method (RPM) is a revolutionary breakthrough in time and life management. This custom-designed planner will help you implement RPM in your daily life, giving you the freedom and peace of mind to pursue your true passions.

Includes: Elegant and durable RPM binder featuring zipper closure and pockets for convenient storage, 365 dated daily forms, 12 tabbed monthly calendars, extra planning forms and Quick Start Guide.

PERSONAL POWER® II
30TH ANNIVERSARY EDITION
30-Day Program That Provides Systematic Strategies to Get Greater Results on a Daily Basis

Let the top-rated personal and professional development system of all time help you embrace your inner strength to free yourself from daily stresses and simplify your life in ways you never thought possible! Personal Power II will help you identify negative thought patterns impeding your personal and professional progress so you can break through your personal barriers to achievement.

Includes: 25 CDs, a custom Success Journal, $100 coupon good toward the purchase of any live multi-day Anthony Robbins event.

CREATING LASTING CHANGE
10-Day Program to Maximum Impact

The 7 Steps to Maximum Impact guides you down the path to becoming a more effective inspirational leader. In this 10-day program, you will examine leadership from a unique perspective—the ability to influence the thoughts, feelings and actions of others.

Includes: 12 audio CDs featuring proven success strategies Anthony Robbins has mastered over the last three decades, bonus DVD and comprehensive workbook.

Call Our Product Specialists: 800.397.6329

MASTERING INFLUENCE™

For Strengthening Your Emotional Impact and Increasing Your Sales

Designed to give you a psychological and emotional advantage over your competition, Mastering Influence will also empower you with the confidence and drive you need to stay focused on your goals.

Includes: Elegant and durable RPM binder featuring zipper closure and pockets for convenient storage, 12 CDs, a 100-page workbook, flash cards and a bonus Unleash the Power Within *sneak preview DVD.*

LOVE AND PASSION®
ULTIMATE RELATIONSHIP PROGRAM™

10 Steps to Create, Transform and Celebrate the Greatest Gift of Life

A loving, passionate and intimate relationship can be sometimes challenging to sustain. This program guides you through six sessions, each focusing on one of these vital skills: Understanding, Giving, Trust, Intimacy, Honesty and Alignment.

Includes: 6 full-length DVD films, 4 audio CDs, action workbook and a bonus inspirational DVD.

THE PATH TO PERMANENT WEIGHT LOSS

How many people do you know who are hoping that a new diet will "motivate" them to lose weight? How many people do you know who have already given up on the last diet and are shopping for a new one? The secret to weight loss is not a new diet, the real secret lies in finding the part of yourself that will make the change happen. In this new six-day program you will discover how to tap into your own personal power, trigger a revolution in your health and reclaim the body you deserve.

Includes: 2 audio CDs, 4 Breakthrough DVDs, Success Journal, 12 Urge Buster Cards, and Bonus DVD.

LIVING HEALTH®

What good is having powerful goals if you don't have the energy to carry them out? Anthony Robbins Living Health system will teach you how to adopt a set of simple, enjoyable and powerful principles to create a physically vibrant life with energy that you may have never thought possible.

Includes: 9 audio tracks, Summary Cards and a custom Workbook.

Call Our Product Specialists: 800.397.6329

LIFE BALANCE PACK

Designed to help your body maintain optimal function during a cleanse, the Life Balance Pack replenishes your body with the nutritional support required for a fresh start! This pack includes:

- Inner Clear
- Cranberry Clear
- Probiotics
- Natural Defense
- Senna Tea
- BONUS 5-Pack Pure Energy Greens
- Quick Start Guide—Online

LIVING LIGHT PACK

Lose weight naturally and permanently with the synergistic blend of bioenergetic nutrients and essential compounds found in the Living Light Pack. This pack includes:

- Inner Fuel
- Chromium and Vanadium
- Re-Energize
- Glucommanan
- BONUS 5-Pack Pure Energy Greens
- Quick Start Guide—Online

DAILY ESSENTIALS PACK

Restore your body's natural state of vibrancy and peak efficiency with the essential vitamins, minerals and oils found in the Daily Essentials Pack. This pack includes:

- Daily Essentials Multi-Vitamin
- Probiotics
- Vegetable Harvest
- Citrus Harvest
- Master Oils
- BONUS 5-Pack Pure Energy Greens
- Quick Start Guide

INNER BALANCE
PURE ENERGY GREENS WITH MSM

Increases Energy Levels

A specially formulated blend of organic green vegetables and natural fibers that helps return the blood and tissues to a healthy pH balance, Pure Energy Greens with MSM contains methylsulfonylmethane (MSM), a powerful and natural ingredient that energizes cells and helps alleviate everyday symptoms associated with seasonal allergies.

Please call or visit us online for additional information on our entire line of dietary supplements.

Call Our Product Specialists: 800.397.6329

ANTHONY ROBBINS
coaching
⟩VISION ⟩ACTION ⟩RESULTS

Accelerate Results with Life Coaching
Develop a clear massive action plan to transform your life.

What Is Life Coaching?

Imagine the life you've always dreamed of living, with no barriers or boundaries. Imagine a life rich with success and achievement, endless physical vitality, heartfelt personal relationships and a deep sense of spiritual fulfillment.

Anthony Robbins has studied and developed patterns of success for more than three decades, and his dream to share his results for life transformation laid the groundwork for the Anthony Robbins Coaching program. The custom coaching program will allow you to discover and implement change using the same tools, techniques and methodologies that have enabled world statesmen, high-level business leaders, entrepreneurs and famous athletes to radically transform their businesses and lives.

"The impact of coaching on my entire life has been incredible! My coach helped me figure out what I really wanted and how to get there. It was what I needed to regain my momentum and push through to the next level in all areas of my life!"

— SANDY DRESSER
Senior Loan Officer
Sunbelt Lending Services
Boca Raton, Florida

Flexibility is the key. Because the coaches are trained in a variety of areas and have the entire arsenal of tools and technologies that Tony has created at their disposal, they have resources that enable you to traverse the full spectrum of what you want to accomplish. This flexibility ensures that your coaching experience is truly phenomenal, because you control and drive the creation of your own unique vision and plan—and you have the additional support of an extraordinary partner, someone there to help you face and overcome any challenges you encounter along the way. Your coach is there to keep you on track and hold you accountable to your goals.

Your personal coach is waiting. Take action now.
Call 800.431.4267 for your FREE Coaching Strategy Session.

TONYROBBINS.COM/COACHING

MAKE A DIFFERENCE

OUR MISSION

The Anthony Robbins Foundation is a nonprofit organization created to empower individuals and organizations to make a significant difference in the quality of life for people who are often forgotten—youth, homeless and hungry, prisoners, elderly and disabled. Our international coalition of caring volunteers provides the vision, the inspiration, the finest resources and the specific strategies needed to empower these important members of our society.

INTERNATIONAL BASKET BRIGADE

What began more than 30 years ago as Tony's individual effort to feed families in need has now grown into the Anthony Robbins Foundation's International Basket Brigade, providing baskets of food and household items for more than 3 million people annually in countries all over the world, throughout the Thanksgiving and holiday season.

THE POWER OF YOU

The Anthony Robbins Foundation wholeheartedly supports several outreach programs designed to create positive change in the lives of people who simply need a boost envisioning a happier and deeply satisfying way of life.

There are countless ways the Anthony Robbins Foundation can benefit from your generosity. Donate your time, expertise and wisdom. Give resources and money. Or simply share your ideas and thoughts with us—this alone is the first step in helping those in need discover their own power within. Let's get creative and make change happen together!

We all have the power to share.

THE POWER OF PARTICIPATING

To find out how you can create powerful change that transforms lives—or to send a tax-deductible donation—contact the Anthony Robbins Foundation.

CELEBRATING

30

YEARS *of*
CONTRIBUTION

"Contribution is not an obligation; it's an opportunity to give something back."

—ANTHONY ROBBINS

For More Information, Call 800.554.0619